The Wind in the Willows

A Family Entertainment

John Morley

Based on *The Wind in the Willows*
by Kenneth Grahame

Samuel French - London
New York - Toronto - Hollywood

CHARACTERS

Toad
Ratty
Mole
Mr Badger
The Chief Weasel

The following parts can be doubled, if required:
Dobbin, the Horse
Mrs Otter
Portly Otter, her young son
Reginald ⎫
Fiona ⎭ Edwardian motorists
High Court Magistrate
High Court Clerk
High Court Policeman
Jenny, the policeman's daughter
Nelly ⎫
Maggie ⎪
Ada ⎪ Jenny's aunts
Flo ⎪ (see note on page ix)
Patsy ⎪
Clementina ⎭
Bargewoman
Zelda, leader of the gypsies

Chorus of:
Good Animals—rabbits, field-mice and perhaps squirrels
Bad Animals—wicked weasels, ferrets and perhaps stoats
Gypsies

ACT I
Scene 1   The Riverbank and the Willows
Scene 2   The Corridor leading to the Courtroom
Scene 3(a) The Courtroom at the Castle
Scene 3(b) "The Hole"—a dismal dungeon

ACT II
Scene 1   The Canal bank near the Castle
Scene 2   The Gypsy Camp further along the Canal
Scene 3   The Riverbank again
Scene 4   Inside Toad Hall

Period: Edwardian Summertime

MUSICAL NUMBERS

Permission to perform this play DOES NOT include permission to use copyright songs and music (here denoted by an asterisk). Please read the notice supplied by the Performing Right Society very carefully.

The songs listed below are *only suggestions* for the type of music that can be used in this pantomime. Choice of music and songs is left to the discretion of the individual producer.

OVERTURE   Song 5

ACT I

1(a)	*Cruising Down the River	Rabbits and Field-mice
1(b)	*Row, Row, Row (ragtime production routine)	Ratty and the Animals
2	Toad's Song (parody of *The British Grenadiers*)	Toad and the Animals
3	*Run, Rabbit, Run	
	or	
	The Ghost's High Noon (from *Ruddigore*)	Weasels
	or	
	*a "wicked sounding" rock number	
4(a)	Bow Ye Lower Middle Classes (from *Iolanthe*)	Company
4(b)	I've Got A Little List (parody from *The Mikado*)	Judge and Company
5	*Get Out and Get Under (The Motor Car Song)	Toad and Company
6	*My Old Man (Said Follow the Van)	Jenny's Aunts

ACT II

7	*Out of Town	
	or	
	*The Entertainer Rag (Scott Joplin)	Rabbits and Field-mice
	or	
	*I Like Country Music (with a rustic dance that is almost a square dance)	
8	Chase Music. Any Offenbach Can-Can or the William Tell Overture	Bargewoman and Rabbits
9	Dance a Cachucha (parody from *The Gondoliers*)	Gypsies
10	*Jealousy	
	or	
	*Twist and Shout	Weasels
	or	
	*In The Mood	

11	Victory For Toad (parody of *Phil The Fluter's Ball*)	Company
12	Reprise of Song 5	Company
Finale	Reprise of Song 6	Company

A licence issued by Samuel French Ltd to perform this play does NOT include permission to use any copyright music in the performance. The notice printed below on behalf of the Performing Right Society should be carefully read. In case of difficulty in finding sheet music, FRANCIS MUSIC SUPPLY of Gerrard Street, London, W1, are usually most helpful.

The following statement concerning the use of music is printed here on behalf of the Performing Right Society Ltd, by whom it was supplied

The permission of the owner of the performing right in copyright music must be obtained before any public performance may be given, whether in conjunction with a play or sketch or otherwise, and this permission is just as necessary for amateur performances as for professional. The majority of copyright musical works (other than oratorios, musical plays and similar dramatico-musical works) are controlled in the British Commonwealth by the PERFORMING RIGHT SOCIETY LTD, 29–33 Berners Street, London W1P 4AA.

The Society's practice is to issue licences authorizing the use of its repertoire to the proprietors of premises at which music is publicly performed, or, alternatively, to the organizers of musical entertainments, but the Society does not require payment of fees by performers as such. Producers or promoters of plays, sketches, etc., at which music is to be performed, during or after the play or sketch, should ascertain whether the premises at which their performances are to be given are covered by a licence issued by the Society, and if they are not, should make application to the Society for particulars as to the fee payable.

Flexible Casting
This family entertainment is for five main principals. There are ten other parts but they can be doubled. The adult and/or juvenile chorus play the small parts.

Because the story is a fantasy (the animals speak and are human sized) it is possible to have an all-female cast, an all-male cast or a mixed cast. The casting is adaptable, too, for the Magistrate can become female as can the Policeman, and all the animals may be female.

You may find that audience involvement is clearer and costume problems are simpler with just Weasels (as "baddies") and Rabbits (as "goodies") and that the other chorus animals mentioned in Kenneth Grahame's *The Wind in the Willows* are not needed.

Setting
The entire story can be played in a permanent set, or in-the-round, with no scenery at all.

The principals have no costume change. The chorus costumes are rabbits, then weasels, then gypsies.

Please refer to the detailed scenery and costume notes at the end of the script

DESCRIPTION OF CHARACTERS

Toad is boisterous, hearty, with a comically grating laugh ("Har har har"), swaggering, jaunty, not too brainy, amazingly conceited but a kind and warmhearted soul, so he is popular. He has a butterfly brain that flits from one craze to the next. He is devoted to his home, Toad Hall. Particularly in the first scene he should walk about with strange galumping strides—as if wearing flippers—to suggest how a Toad would indeed walk.

Ratty is cheerful, energetic, efficient, frank in his criticisms, and nautical, for he is besotted about the river and the boats on it.

Mole is gentle, easily impressed, shy and loyal. He stands with his toes turned in but his paws, being a mole's, are strong. He wears thick rimmed glasses. Male or female part.

Badger is stolid, a bit condescending but a nice old buffer and older than the others so he is a father figure. He plods along, usually with a clumsy-looking walking stick, like a farmer and perhaps he has a mild rustic accent.

The Chief Weasel is insolent, loud, aggressive, ambitious and scheming. He is a 1908 gangster and we realize why all the Riverbankers are scared of him.

Dobbin the Horse is almost a pantomime horse—no dialogue—but he has character. He is sensitive and "doesn't like to be left out of things". A part for two females, perhaps?

Reginald and Fiona are Edwardian motorists. They are written as an upper class, silly couple, but you can easily localize them to Welsh, Glaswegian, Geordie—some local accent, if this is fun for your audience.

The Magistrate is eccentric, comical, brisk and prejudiced against Toad. Male or female part.

The Clerk wears glasses on the end of his nose, is a fool and a bit spiteful. Male or female part.

The Policeman is red-faced, preferably fat and clumsy, and is dim, with either a Cockney accent, or a comedy version of some local accent.

The Magistrate, Clerk and **Policeman** are not just comedy characters. They should appreciate that they are in fact Toad's enemies until half way through Act Two.

Mrs Otter should really be sleek, just as all otters are, but it is more important to play her as a fussy and much worried mum.

Portly Otter is as young as possible and there are deliberately few lines for him (or her) due to this age factor. The moment when Mrs Otter and her young son are reconciled is highly emotional if a very young child plays Portly. Portly doesn't walk, he waddles.

Jenny the Policeman's daughter is intelligent, vivacious and kind. Mild Cockney or "local" accent.

Jenny's six Aunts These six washerwomen (or fewer if preferred) plus Jenny and the Policeman are all the same family, so whatever accent you choose for one applies to all. The main moment for the Aunts is a Cockney "knees-up" song, so Cockney seems best for this family. Their scene can be played with only two Aunts if preferred; or just one Aunt can be used. See alternative scene on p.31.

The Bargewoman is a fat country woman, with a cruel streak.

Zelda is a weird old gypsy hag, extrovert, shrewd and clearly the leader of the Gypsies.

THE CHORUS

The Good Animals (Rabbits etc.) have a Beatrix Potter warmth and charm. **The Bad Animals** (Weasels etc.) are cocky, sniggering, energetic 1908 gangsters.

The Gypsies are poor and desperate but extrovert and noisy.

Note All the animals hold their hands up at chest level, as though paws. When the animals are pleased, or are gloating, they jump in the air several times.

ACT I

Overture

SCENE 1

The Riverbank and the Willows

Song 1(A)

All the animals are on stage singing Song 1(a). Field-mice run with small paces, Squirrels run with paws held up high and eyes darting about. More animals enter and wave greetings to each other. The adults have parasols or carry straw boaters, giving an impression of the animal version of a summer afternoon in 1908

After a chorus the music continues under the dialogue as one of the Rabbits points offstage

1st Rabbit Eeeek! Eeeek! Look who's on the river!
2nd Rabbit Who is it?
1st Rabbit It's the Water Rat!

All turn to each other excitedly

> *They cheer as Ratty, wearing a jaunty nautical cap, enters upstage, sitting behind a cut-out of a blue rowing boat, miming as though he is rowing. Then he stops, and waves*

Ratty (*calling over the music*) Ship ahoy! Hove to! Hullo, animals!
All Hullo Ratty!

Two of the Field-mice help Ratty as he jumps out of his boat

Two Field-mice Eeek! Eeek! Hullo, Mr Ratty!
Ratty Hullo you two! Belay there! (*To all*) Enjoying yourselves?
All Yes!
1st Rabbit It's a lovely day, that's why!
Ratty It's a lovely day all right! Lovely for rowing on the river! (*He sings, at fast ragtime tempo, with rowing actions*)

Song 1(B)

Everyone joins in and the song becomes

Ragtime Production Routine

After the routine ends Mrs Otter loudly bursts into tears, takes out a handkerchief and wipes her eyes

Ratty Well, shiver me timbers, what's up, Mrs Otter?

Mrs Otter (*greatly distressed*) Oh, Ratty, it's my little boy. He's missing!

Ratty Little Portly?

Mrs Otter (*nodding*) Why am I here when I ought to be looking for him? I must go.

Ratty But he's just a young otter! He's gone off to play somewhere!

All (*agreeing*) That's right! He'll be back soon! It's all right Mrs Otter!

Mrs Otter (*shaking her head; scared*) I'm wondering if little Portly has been kidnapped by *them*.

Ratty "Them"? (*To the others*) She means the Weasels and the Stoats!

There is a dramatic chord and everyone clutches each other in terror

All The Weasels and the Stoats!

Ratty Haven't you heard the terrible news?

All What's that?

Ratty The Chief Weasel says he's not content with living in the Wild Wood anymore! He wants to take over the Riverbank from here right down to Toad Hall! (*He gestures off*)

1st Rabbit Then we'd better look for little Portly!

Ratty Yes, I think we had! (*Putting an arm around Mrs Otter's shoulder*) Now, *don't worry* Mrs Otter—we'll find Portly won't we?

All Yes!

Ratty So, easy does it. Keep on an even keel. There, there.

All start to exit, urgently talking to each other, Ratty still with his arm round Mrs Otter's shoulder

All (*solo lines*) The Chief Weasel is the trouble!

The Weasels and the Ferrets have captured Portly!

We must search everywhere!

Poor Little Portly!

Never trust a Weasel or a Stoat!

Come on—we must find Portly!

As the animals exit, there is dramatic music, the Lights darken and in a green spot-light the Chief Weasel runs in, pointing viciously to the animals

Chief Weasel (*triumphantly*) There they go—the Rabbits and the River-bankers—and each one is frightened to death of the Chief Weasel! (*He laughs cruelly*) Ha, ha, ha! Oh, but I must introduce myself. I *am* the Chief Weasel. (*He strolls across the stage*) I'm slimy, sinister and sarcastic. I'm deadly, distasteful and disasterous. Oh, I forgot, I'm *ambitious* as well. So I've made some poisonous little plans. (*He points off right*) I'm going to invade the valley, conquer the countryside, and *rule over the Riverbank*! My followers are the ferrets, the weasels and the stoats, and if any other dear little cuddly animals get in my way, they'll live to regret it! And that includes Little Portly. I haven't found him yet, but when I do I'll use him as a hostage. (*Sarcastically*) Poor Little Portly. I've an idea he's lost in the Wild Wood—(*with relish*)—I do hope so. (*He makes his hand like claws*) I can't wait to get my paws on poor ... little ... Portly. Then there'll be trouble—and trouble's my favourite word! Ha, ha, ha!

Chief Weasel claws the air at the Audience then exits left to dramatic music

Ratty enters right

Ratty (*calling*) Ahoy there! Portly! Where are you Portly? (*Seeing someone about to enter*) Ah, are you Portly?

Mole enters very timidly. He is holding a bucket with white-wash splashed on it. He stands with his toes turned in and blinks a lot, and bites his nails

(*Breezily*) Oh—hullo!
Mole (*shyly*) Hullo. It's a nice day. (*He takes a big brush from the bucket and mimes painting a wall*) I was working very hard, white-washing my little home, doing the spring cleaning, when I suddenly thought "Hang spring cleaning!" (*He puts the brush in the bucket and bangs it on the floor, and then makes mole tunnelling gestures with his paws*) I sensed Spring was here, so I tunnelled upwards out of my hole. I scraped and scratched and scrabbled and scrooged till POP! My snout popped out! I'd hit the daylight! (*He lifts up his nose and blinks at the sunlight*)
Ratty (*laughing*) So you're a mole! Good morning, Mole!
Mole Good morning Rat. (*He gazes round, beaming*) Oh my! Oh my! Oh my! I am enjoying myself. How exciting the world is! I've just seen a big blue log in the river. (*He points upstage*)
Ratty (*shocked*) A big blue log? That's my boat!
Mole I'm sorry, I've never seen a boat before.
Ratty (*shocked even more*) What?
Mole (*shyly*) Is it very nice?
Ratty *NICE?*

Ratty brings Mole downstage talking expansively with great enthusiasm

It's the *only* thing! Believe me, my young friend there is *nothing*— absolutely nothing—half so much worth doing as simply messing about in boats. (*Dreamily*) Simply messing ... messing about in boats ... all Spring. (*He comes out of his dream*) What have *you* been doing all Spring?
Mole (*making digging gestures with his paws*) Making mole-hills. I lead a very quiet life. (*Gesturing further*) I burrow.

Palms outwards, Mole mimes pushing earth aside, and then sticks his head forward peering intently out front. Ratty watches with interest.

Ratty So where do you live?
Mole (*pointing off*) In the fields near Toad Hall.

Ratty nods recognition

Ratty And then you wanted some fresh air, so you weighed anchor—heave ho—and you toddled down here to the River Bank! Welcome to The Willows!

Mole Thank you, Ratty. (*He looks around*) So *these* are the Willows. (*Pointing off*) But what are those trees over there?

Ratty (*suddenly nervous*) Oh nothing, nothing, don't talk about them.

Mole But it's only a wood!

Ratty It's the *Wild* Wood.

There is a dramatic chord

Mole (*alarmed*) The Wild Wood—I've heard of it.

Ratty There are some *nice* animals in the Wood—just as there are in any wood—but, mainly it's the home of the ferrets, the stoats, the weasels—and their leader, The Chief Weasel.

Mole The Chief Weasel—I've heard of him as well!

Ratty (*grimly*) I'm sure you have. Oh, shipmate, if only there was someone to challenge him, to stop him *threatening* us Riverbankers—but who is that someone?

Mole Don't look at me. I'm a mole, a gentle soul, and I'm scared! (*He bites his nails anxiously*)

Ratty Cheer up matey! There may be a storm blowing on the starboard but why should we let the Chief Weasel rule our lives? (*He claps his hands together in sudden inspiration*) Mole, why don't we go on the river?

Mole is delighted and jumps up in the air

Mole Oh, yes! What a day I'm having!

Ratty We'll take a picnic!

Mole Oh my! Oh my! Oh my! (*Excited, he marches and stamps about and consequently puts his foot in the white-wash bucket*)

Mole (*gloomily*) Oh my . . .

Mole takes his foot out, pulling a face. Ratty laughs

I'm fed up with whitewash. (*He picks up the bucket deposits it in the wings and returns*)

Ratty (*as he goes*) So you'd like a picnic! I'll get the picnic basket—it is packed—there's a red tablecloth and white plates and green lettuce and brown bread and blue cheese and pink blancmange and yellow custard and—

Ratty exits

Mole is squirming with delight at the sound of all the food

Mole Oh my! Oh my! Oh my! This is better than spring cleaning! (*He lies on the floor and bicycles with his feet*) A picnic with a tablecloth! Oh my! Oh my! Oh my!

Ratty staggers in with a heavy basket and plonks it down CS

Ratty What are you doing down there?

Mole (*getting up*) I'm happy, that's all. (*He sees the basket*) Oh, I say!

Ratty I'm afraid it's only a snack lunch. Just (*like a verbal waterfall*) cold tongue, cold ham, cold chicken, cold beef, pickled gherkins, salad, French rolls, watercress sandwiches, potted meat, ginger ale, lemonade——
Mole (*in an ecstasy*) Oh stop! Stop! This is too much!
Ratty (*laughing*) Come on, help me with it to the boat, then we'll set sail.

They start to pick up the basket when a Field-mouse runs on waving a small Union Jack

1st Field-mouse (*in a piping voice*) Hooray!

Another Field-mouse runs on also waving a Union Jack

2nd Field-mouse Hooray!

Others, mainly the juvenile animals, run on cheering and waving small flags

Ratty What are you all cheering for?
1st Field-mouse For Mr Toad!
Ratty But why are you cheering *Toad*?
2nd Field-mouse He gave us a penny each if we'd cheer him, so (*loudly*) hooray!
3rd Field-mouse (*chanting*) Mr Toad's coming! Mr Toad's coming! Mr Toad's coming!
Mole Is that Mr Toad who lives at Toad Hall?
Ratty Yes—and I've just realized something. If Toad sees the picnic basket, we're sunk! He'll eat the lot! Come on!

They close the lid, pick up the picnic basket and are about to exit but Toad enters, with his huge galumping strides, royally waving to the Field-mice

Toad Hullo! Hullo! Thank you for your greetings. And so spontaneous too! (*With his hearty laugh*) Har, har, har! Why, hullo Ratty! (*He shakes Ratty's hand heartily*) And who is this?
Mole (*quietly*) I'm Mole.
Toad Well, you can't help it! We all make mistakes sometimes! Even I do! Har, har, har! I'm Toad, you're Mole—shake a paw! (*He heartily shakes hands, but breaks off quickly*) OW! (*He wrings his hand with the pain*)
Mole I'm sorry. My hands are rather strong—I need them for burrowing. (*He gestures with his hands like flippers, as before*) As I said, I'm Mole.
Toad Well, I'm Toad. The handsome, the popular, the successful Toad! (*To the Field-mice*) Right?
Field-mice Right! (*They wave their flags*)
Toad Clever Toad, great Toad, *good* Toad—right?
Field-mice Right!
Ratty (*to Mole*) You'll never believe this, but underneath it all he's a very nice fellow!

Toad moves CS *with the Field-mice on each side of him. Ratty and Mole move to a downstage corner and watch, Ratty disapprovingly*

Toad (*miming blowing a trumpet*) Ta—ta—ta—ta!
Field-mice (*with the same gesture* Ta—ta—ta—ta!

The music sounds a fanfare now, and Toad sings as the Rabbits and Field-mice mark time "stationary marching".

Song 2

Toad   The world has held great heroes
                    As history books have showed
                    But never a name with a claim to fame
                    Compared to that of Toad
                    The clever men at Oxford
                    Know all there is to be knowed
                    But none of them know how to put on a show
                    Compared to Mister Toad.

Field-mice   But none of them know how to put on a show
                    Compared to Mister Toad.

Toad   The soldiers all saluted
                    As they marched along the road
                    And did they cheer the Brigadier?
                    No—it was Mister Toad
                    The sailors in the Navy
                    Saluted as they rowed
                    Was it the Queen that they had seen?
                    No—it was Mister Toad

Field-mice   Was it the Queen that they had seen?
                    No—it was Mister Toad.

                    They do a short routine of marching and then:

Toad   You've heard of Boadicea
                    With her chariot covered in woad
                    She was brave and fair but she couldn't compare
                    With victorious Mister Toad.
                    And what about Napoleon
                    As into battle he strode—
                    Well, he met his Waterloo which Toad didn't do
                    Oh, wonderful Mister Toad.

Field-mice   Well, he met his Waterloo which Toad didn't do
                    Oh, wonderful Mister Toad.

Coda, with much waving of flags:

                    That wonderful, victorious
                    And absolutely glorious
                    Clever Mister Toad!!!

Ratty (*to Mole, after the song*) Doesn't it make you sea-sick?

Toad (*to the others*) Field-mice, Rabbits, Countrymen—lend me your ears!
I won't be needing you any more today. But when I want another
spontaneous welcome, I'll contact you! Goodbye my friends! Har, har,
har!

Field-mice ⎫ (*together; in high pitched voices*)   Goodbye, Mr Toad!
Rabbits ⎭

The Field-mice and Rabbits exit but one Field-mouse runs back

Field-mouse Mister Toad . . .

Toad Yes, my boy?

Field-mouse You gave us all a penny but I've lost mine and I wanted to buy
some nuts with it.

Toad Are you telling the truth?

Field-mouse Oh, yes, Mister Toad. Cross my heart. (*He crosses his heart*)

Toad All right. Here's a shilling.

Field-mouse Oh, thank you, Mr Toad. You are generous.

The Field-mouse exits

Toad That's me all over. Generous, warmhearted, charming—what more
could you want?

Ratty Modesty. My friend Mole and I are wondering what you're doing so
far from Toad Hall. (*Warningly*) You must take care Toad, the Chief
Weasel's been seen skulking about.

Toad Oh, pooh! (*He gives a dismissive gesture*)

Ratty Besides, I've never seen you walk anywhere before.

Toad My dear Ratty, I didn't *walk*. (*To Mole*) Can you imagine a *toad*
walking? No, I came here by transport.

Ratty Oh, matey, don't tell me you've bought another bicycle? (*To Mole*)
He's had six and smashed them all.

Toad (*airily*) Oh no, no, no.

Ratty Another motor bike? (*To Mole*) He's got through eight of those.

Toad There's a huge pile of smashed-up motor bikes at home! It must be the
largest pile of smashed-up motor bikes in the world! (*Laughing proudly*)
Har, har, har! (*To Mole*) I never do anything by halves.

Ratty Don't I know it! (*With an ominous and serious warning*) One of these
days Toad, you'll end up in trouble—*terrible* trouble.

Toad Oh pooh! (*He pulls a face*) Pooh, pooh, pooh, pooh, pooh.

Mole Then how *did* you get here Mr Toad? It took me hours, but then, I've
only got short legs.

Toad Ah! I got here the *new* way, the *only* way. Excuse me. (*Toad takes a
whistle on a string round his neck and blows it*)

Ratty (*to Mole*) I'm dreading this. It'll be the latest of his crazes—
something garish and expensive and probably *highly dangerous*.

*Dobbin the Horse neighs as he enters—to coconut shells hoof-beat effects—
pulling on a cut-out of a vividly painted yellow caravan*

(*Groaning*) What did I tell you? (*Pointing to the caravan*) Toad's latest
craze.

Mole (*impressed*) Oh my! Oh my! Oh my!

Toad A luxury caravan and a luxury horse to go with it! (*To Dobbin*) Now Dobbin, say hullo to everyone! (*Aside; to the others*) He doesn't like to be left out, you know.

Dobbin neighs and nods to Mole and Ratty, who nod back, then he looks at the Audience and decides to nod to them also

(*Pointing proudly to the caravan*) There you are—my caravan! Remember my luxury yacht? My beautiful boat? My push-bike? My motor-bike? But now, who cares about such things?

Ratty Toad ...

Toad There's *real* life for you, embodied in this lovely caravan!

Dobbin glares at Toad and neighs

Oh, embodied in this lovely horse as well! (*Aside; to the others*) He doesn't like to be left out, you know.

Mole Then I'll let him out of the shafts.

Mole removes Dobbin from the shafts, strokes his head and brings him downstage. Meanwhile Toad is downstage pacing to and fro, followed by Ratty trying to keep up with him. As Toad declaims and the others listen, so the Tabs slowly close behind them and Toad, Ratty, Mole and Dobbin are in front of Tabs or a wood-land frontcloth

Toad What a time we shall have! The open road, the dusty highway, the heath, the common, the hedgerows, the rolling downs!

Ratty Toad ...

Toad Finest caravan that was ever built—without exception. And why? I designed it all myself, I did.

Ratty Toad, you don't think it might be *dangerous* in some way?

Toad Dangerous? Oh, I hope so! Har, har, har! (*To Mole*) Life is one long adventure to be lived recklessly! Don't you agree?

Mole Well ... er ...

Ratty No, he doesn't. He's a quiet person, unlike some people I know. Now, this caravan ...

Toad Oh yes. (*He paces about again*) Well, it's full of pots, pans, jugs, kettles, biscuits, potted lobster, sardines, soda water, jam, a set of dominoes—anything you could possibly want!

Ratty I don't like it.

Toad So we now start on our adventures!

Ratty Did you say "WE" start?

Toad My dear old Ratty, don't talk in that sniffy sort of way, because you know you've got to come!

Ratty But ...

Toad Now, don't argue—it's the one thing I can't stand. You *surely* don't mean to stick to your dull old river all your life, and just live on a *boat*? We're going to see villages, towns, cities—aren't we Dobbin?

Dobbin nods and neighs

He doesn't like to be left out, you know.

Mole is thrilled, clapping his hands together and jumping up and down

Mole Oh my! Oh my! Oh my!
Toad I want to show you the world!
Mole Oooooo!
Ratty (*incredulously*) Well, stow the tackle. You don't actually *want* to go with Toad, do you?
Mole Er ... (*He sees Ratty's face*) I'll always stick by you Ratty. After you've been so kind to me, I must be loyal.

During Toad's next speech the sound of a period car approaching is heard. Loud shouts of "Look out" "Careful!" "What are you doing?" "Help!" are heard from behind the Tabs or frontcloth. Then there is a great crash, percussion effects and loud discords of music

Toad I understand about loyalty. Jolly good thing in its way. But fellows, this is a caravan holiday! (*Calling out in ecstasy*) The bright blue sky, the sunshine, the camp-fire, the wind whistling past your ears, the breezes round your kneezes—
Mole
Ratty } (*together; apprehensively*) What was that?
Toad

Toad, Mole, Ratty and Dobbin turn and face upstage. The Tabs open to reveal the yellow caravan on its side with a wheel off and the brightly coloured shutters broken (see production notes at end of script). Mole and Ratty rush upstage to inspect the caravan, but Toad runs and stands by the wings, looking off

Mole (*aghast*) Oh my! Oh my! Oh my!
Ratty It isn't a caravan, it's a catastrophe!

Dobbin jumps up and down and shivers with fright, knocking knees

Mole It's all over now, Dobbin!
Ratty (*to Dobbin*) It's all right, shipmate. I know the car hit the caravan, but it didn't hit *you!*
Mole (*realizing*) Toad's beautiful caravan, wrecked by a motorist.
Ratty (*shouting off, beyond Toad, and shaking his fist*) You villain! You scoundrel! You roadhog! You—you—you *motorist!* I'll have the law on you! You've wrecked the caravan and you've wrecked my friend Toad! He'll never be the same again!

Toad turns round, deep in thought, head down. It seems to be a tragedy as he walks CS

Mole (*with much sympathy*) Aaaaaah ...
Ratty Aaaaaaah ...
Mole (*gently*) Toad—is there anything you'd like to say?
Ratty (*gently*) Toad, can we help, me old shipmate? Speak to us, Toad.

As Toad holds up his head, we see he is in ecstasy

Toad Poop poop! Poop poop!
Ratty
Mole } (*together*) Eh?

Toad Poop, poop! Poop poop! (*Pacing about*) Glorious, stirring sight! The poetry of motion! The *real* way to travel! The *only* way to travel! (*With great enthusiasm*) A motor car! Villages skipped, towns and cities jumped! Here today—gone in a second—whoosh! Not only whoosh, but also poop poop! Poop poop!

Ratty Toad, stop being an ass. Look at the caravan window! Look at the roof!

Dobbin glares and neighs

Look at Dobbin!

Toad (*in a trance of delight*) To think I never *knew*! To think I never *dreamt*! But now I know what fast roads lie ahead of me! What dust and petrol fumes as I speed on my reckless way! What caravans I shall hit! Horrid caravans—common caravans—canary coloured caravans! All shall be crashed into! All! All! (*He stands still with a stupid looking smile on his face*)

Mole (*staring at the gormless Toad*) What a dreadful thing to say! What shall we do with him?

Ratty (*defeated*) Nothing. I know him of old. He is now possessed. (*With a great groan*) He's got another craze.

Toad (*staring into oblivion*) Poop poop! Poop poop!

Mole (*with much concern*) But he's in some terrible trance. You must help him.

Toad (*gormlessly*) Poop poop! Poop—(*He comes to*) I've just remembered Dobbin. (*Patting Dobbin's head*) Dear old Dobbin, I won't be needing you now. You see, motor cars don't need a horse to pull them. But don't worry, I'll find you a good home!

Dobbin is pleased, so frisks about as Toad turns to the others

He doesn't like to be left out, you know.

Ratty And another thing—telephone the police about the caravan crash!

Mole (*agreeing*) Yes, telephone the police!

Toad (*incredulously*) Telephone the police? I shall telephone to order a motor car. And I'll do it right now!

Ratty WHAT?

Toad (*with loud bravado*) A large and expensive motor car—with a large and expensive motor horn on it! (*He mimes squeezing the horn's bulb*) Poop poop! Poop poop! Poop poop!

Toad exits

Ratty Toad! Come back at once! Toad! Shipmate! Belay there!

Ratty exits, furious with Toad, and Dobbin follows him

Mole (*starting to follow; calling*) Toad! Ratty! Dobbin!

Mrs Otter enters

Mole does not see Mrs Otter. The stage becomes dark and sinister

Mrs Otter (*calling out anxiously*) Portly!

Mole (*calling*) Portly! (*He realizes what he is saying. To himself*) Who's
    Portly?
Mrs Otter Portly is my son! I've looked everywhere for him, but he's lost!
Mole I'm sure someone will find him ...
Mrs Otter Yes—the Weasels and Ferrets will! They're not content with the
    Wild Wood any longer—they want to take over the Riverbank as well!
Mole Oh, that's only a rumour. Are you Mrs Otter?
Mrs Otter Yes—and I can see you're Mr Mole.
Mole I am, and you've nothing to worry about. Nothing at all. Truly.

*A Weasel jumps out from the wings, waggles its hands and disappears again.
Drum beats start*

Mrs Otter (*clutching at Mole*) What was that?
Mole What was what?
Mrs Otter I saw a weasel.
Mole Oh, I don't think so.

*Other Weasels spookily jump out from the wings and exit again. There will
probably be audience participation here. After this business with audience:*

Mrs Otter (*looking round warily*) The Wild Wooders are on the prowl.

Another Weasel jumps out and stands in a sinister attitude

There! Did you see that?
Mole (*cheerfully*) No! (*He now sees the Weasel*) Yes! (*Scared*) You'd better
    come with me Mrs Otter! This is no time for a chat—we must hide!

Mole shepherds Mrs Otter downstage

Mrs Otter Oh—poor Portly! Poor little Portly! My dear boy!

*As they both hide at the downstage corner there is dramatic music, lightning,
thunder and dim lighting as the Chief Weasel jumps on stage and energeti-
cally beckons on the Wild Wooders*

Chief Weasel (*shouting over the drumbeat music and effects*) Ferrets, follow
    me! Stoats, step this way! Weasels, well done! (*With a grand gesture*)
    Today the Riverbank, tomorrow the World! Ha, ha, ha!

*The Wicked Animals stampede in, and rush about, stamping their feet,
shaking clenched fists, and shouting over the music*

Wicked Animals (*Variously*) Victory!
    Revenge!
    Conquer!
    Murder!
    Pillage!
    Triumph!
    Success!
    Vanquish!
    Yah!

Strobe lighting starts. The Chief Weasel and his followers sing and dance

Song 3

This production number is loud, energetic, frightening and is in the style of a war dance. After it, the Chief Weasel proclaims to the group around him who claw the air with their paws

Chief Weasel Ferocious Ferrets!
All (*shouting*) Yes!
Chief Weasel Wicked Weasels!
All (*shouting*) Yes!
Chief Weasel Stinking Stoats!
All (*shouting*) Yes!
Chief Weasel Come my foul followers—we've danced the Wicked Weasel War Dance, so now to declare war!
All (*shouting*) War!
Chief Weasel Run all over the Riverbank, climb all over the countryside, frolic all over the fields, you loyal and loathesome animals! (*With a great gesture*) Onwards!
All Onwards!

The Chief Weasel points dynamically off, and shouting "Onwards!" "Onwards!" they all stampede off with war cries and shouts

Mole brings Mrs Otter out from hiding. Both are terrified

Mole (*horrified*) They do want to invade us! They do want to conquer the countryside!
Mrs Otter What did I tell you? We must warn Mr Badger! He lives near here.
Mole Mr Badger? Where's his house?
Mrs Otter I'm not sure. We must search.
Mole (*gazing around unhappily*) Yes.

Various Weasel arms stick out from the wings and are slowly waved up and down, then finally disappear

Oooooo, I'm getting scared again, Mrs Otter! The spooky trees, the shadows, the dead leaves all over the ground ...
Mrs Otter (*laughing*) Well at least you won't fall over a dead leaf!
Mole (*loudly*) OW! I just did! (*He hops about*) Oh, my leg! Oh, my poor leg! Oh my! Oh my! Oh my!
Mrs Otter What's wrong?
Mole If I didn't fall over a leaf, I fell over something.

Mrs Otter kneels down and looks at Mole's foot

Mrs Otter Mr Mole, you must have tripped over a hidden branch or a tree stump. Will it go septic?
Mole A septic tree stump?
Mrs Otter Mr Mole, you are silly! (*Examining Mole's foot*) But don't worry,

it's a clean cut. Looks as if it was done by the sharp edge of something in metal.

Mole (*realizing*) Just a minute, Mrs Otter! I'll do some burrowing! I've got an idea! (*He kneels down and burrows very near the wings. Panting*) Oh my! Oh my! I know what it is! I know what it is!

Mrs Otter (*confused*) What are you doing? What's the matter?

Mole What I tripped over was a door scraper! That's why I cut myself! And look, Mrs Otter, hidden under the leaves is the doormat! (*He holds the doormat up—pre-set in the wings*)

Mrs Otter Then Mr Badger's front door must be close by!

Mole (*excitedly*) Oh my! Oh my! Oh my! Look!

Mole puts his hand on a door-knocker that is in fact dimly painted on the tree trunk and hasn't been noticed previously. He mimes using this knocker and a loud knocking sound is heard.

The tree's "secret panel" is slid away and Mr Badger steps forward and "enters" through this big, untidily shaped hole in the tree

Badger (*loudly and gruffly*) Now the next time this happens I shall be extremely angry. Who is it *this* time, disturbing people?

Mole Oh, Mr Badger, it's me, Mr Mole—and my friend, Mrs Otter!

Badger Bless me—it's Mrs Otter.

Mrs Otter Mr Badger, we've come to warn you!

Mole The Wild Wooders are on the warpath!

Mrs Otter And Mr Badger, I know you've been asleep—you spend most of your time asleep—but if you do go for a walk, will you keep a look out for my little Portly? He's—he's— (*She starts to sob*)—he's missing. (*She walks away, much distressed*)

Badger I don't sleep *all* the time, Mrs Otter. And here's something to prove it.

Badger goes back into the tree and re-appears ushering Portly Otter

Mrs Otter (*overwhelmed*) Oh, my podgy little baby!

Portly Hullo, Mum.

Portly steps through the "door" and waddles across to her

Mrs Otter (*caressing him*) Little Portly! Mr Badger, what can I say?

Badger Don't say anything. Go and tell Mr Otter the good news.

Mrs Otter Oh, I will, I will. Portly, say a nice good bye to Mr Mole.

Portly (*waving to Mole*) A nice goodbye!

Mrs Otter And say a big thank you to kind Mr Badger.

Portly (*waving*) A big thank you! (*In a piping voice to Mrs Otter*) Mr Badger gave me a lovely dinner Mum! Far more than you ever give me!

Mrs Otter I'm sure he did, dear. Your Father's watching down by the river, wondering if you've fallen in. Sick with worry he is.

Portly I had soup and fish and twenty four chocolate biscuits!

Mrs Otter Oh, I do feel happy! (*She clasps Portly to her*)

Portly Well, I feel sick!

Mrs Otter Portly dear, come and find your Papa. Thank you Mr Badger, thank you Mr Mole—and bless you both! Portly, your paw ...

Mrs Otter and Portly exit

Badger (*taking the mat from Mole and throwing it into the wings; beaming*) I've wanted to meet you for a long time, Mr Mole.
Mole I live underground, Mr Badger, so I don't meet many people.
Badger (*approving strongly*) I live underground as well! It's the only way to live decently! Now Ratty lives in a house by the river where it's damp, and Toad lives at Toad Hall where it's draughty, but you and I—(*He points downwards*)
Mole I like to burrow, Mr Badger. (*He does his burrowing gestures*)
Badger Oh, so do I, Mr Mole. (*He does similar burrowing gestures*) We're creatures who like our creature comforts!

Badger and Mole both laugh

Ratty enters, pointing off

Ratty Well, splice the mainbrace—Mrs Otter has found Portly!
Badger Little Portly was staying with me, out of harm's way. There's no need for you to worry.
Ratty I'm not worried about *that*. It's not as simple as *that*.
Mole Mr Badger and I have struck up a burrowing acquaintance.
Badger (*beaming*) I'm proud to be able to call him my friend.
Ratty I wish I could say the same thing about Toad.
Badger (*groaning*) Toad! Ah me! I knew his father, I knew his grandfather, I knew his Uncle the Archdeacon! If they were alive, they'd be turning in their graves. What's he up to now?
Ratty From bad to worse.
Mole Poop poop! Poop poop!
Badger I beg your pardon?
Ratty That's the sound of a motor car horn, according to Toad. He's got another craze come over him.
Badger (*looking heavenward*) Oh, not another.
Mole Another.
Badger (*mournfully shaking his head*) Alack! Alack! I sense doom and still more doom. I knew his father, I knew his grandfather, I knew his Uncle the Archdeacon—
Ratty Yes, I *know* you did, Badger, but this craze is for motor cars! He'll insist on driving himself and he's hopeless! Like a ship without a rudder!
Mole Let's hope he'll take a driving course.
Badger (*lugubriously*) It'll be a crash course if he does.
Ratty That's right! (*Indignantly*) When he had the motor bike, after every crash he ended up in hospital, covered in bandages—the pounds of grapes I've taken Toad in hospital!
Mole (*indignantly*) And Ratty's told me the amount of fines he's had to pay. Why, it's too awful to think of!
Badger And his rows with the police! When he received his last fine, his

language was unprintable. Oh, helpless animal! Oh, hapless Toad! I knew
his father, I knew his grandfather, I knew his Uncle—

Ratty We three are his friends, Badger. Oughtn't we to *do* something?

Badger We certainly ought. Where is he now?

Mole In bed I suppose. Recovering from the caravan crash.

Ratty In bed? When I last saw him he was going into the Gentleman's
Outfitters in the village.

Badger Gentleman's Outfitters? I don't like the sound of that. It's ominous.
(*Starting the dirge again*) I knew his father, I knew his grandfather,
I knew ...

Ratty (*edgily*) Badger, what are we going to do? Toad carries on like
anything, quite oblivious, but someone's watching him—*and that
someone is the Chief Weasel.*

Badger (*severely*) Then we'll stand no nonsense about the motor cars. We'll
bring him back to reason, and by force if need be. We'll *make* him be a
sensible Toad. We'll ...

*Toad makes a grand entrance, cheerfully. He is dressed as an Edwardian
motorist with goggles, huge checked cap, long motoring coat and gauntlet
gloves*

Toad's friends are furious

Toad Hullo, you fellows! Come back to Toad Hall with me! My new car
arrives tomorrow—delivered at Toad Hall at ten thirty! Come for a jolly
outing—come for a jolly out ... a jolly ... er—er. ...

The three friends glare at him

Stop staring like that. You're unnerving me!

Badger First of all, take those ridiculous things off.

Toad (*spiritedly*) Shan't! I've just bought 'em!

Ratty |
Mole | (*together*) Take them off!

Toad Do you know who you're talking to? I am Toad! What's more I've
come from the village especially to show you my new motoring gear!

Badger (*wearily*) Take them off him, you two.

Toad How dare you! I'm a *good* Toad, a *kind* Toad! Why, after the caravan
crash, I went home, telephoned the offices of the Grand Union Canal, and
I've got Dobbin a job pulling a barge! He's delighted! Then I thought
about myself, for a change. So I telephoned the offices of the motor car
company and my new automobile will be delivered tomorrow at ...

Badger Take them off him you two, and at once.

Toad But ...

Badger But me no buts. Off with them!

Mole I'm sorry Toad ...

Toad No!

Mole and Ratty chase Toad round the stage

(*Running*) This is disgraceful! I am Toad, the handsome, the popular, the successful—ow! Stop it you two, you're tickling me!
Ratty Mole, you take one sleeve and I'll take the other.

They struggle and all three fall on the floor

Toad (*calling out*) I want to be the Terror of the Highway! I want to crash into everything! Poop poop!
Ratty Sit on him, Mole.
Mole I'm sorry, Toad ...
Toad You've already said you're sorry once—OW!

Mole sits on Toad while Ratty and Badger pull off the motoring coat

It's all so undignified!
Badger You knew it would come to this, sooner or later! You've disregarded all the warnings we gave you when you had the motor bike. You're getting us animals a bad name in the district. Ratty, you can release him now.

Toad stands up minus all the motoring gear and Mole takes goggles, cap, gauntlets and coat and puts them neatly on the ground upstage

Toad, we will leave these two animals for a while. Come with me and hear the facts about yourself. Then we'll see whether you come back the same Toad, or an *improved* Toad. Step this way.
Toad (*meekly*) Yes, Badger. I'm sorry, Badger.
Badger (*ushering him out*) Ah me, I knew your father, I knew your grandfather, I knew your Uncle the Archdeacon. ...

Badger and Toad exit

Ratty (*calling after them contemptuously*) That's no good! Talking to Toad'll never cure him! He'll *say* anything!
Mole Mr Badger will talk to him severely.
Ratty A fat lot of good that'll do.
Mole Listen!

We hear from the wings a loud, stern but unintelligible speech from Badger, which shouldn't be clearly heard but is roughly:

Badger (*off, inaudibly*) I've told you before and I'll tell you again. You must accept more responsibility for your actions. Do you hear me?
Toad (*off, meekly and inaudibly*) Yes, Badger.
Badger (*off, sternly and inaudibly*) I knew your father, I knew your grandfather, I knew your Uncle the Archdeacon.
Toad (*off, inaudibly*) Yes, Badger.
Badger (*off, inaudibly*) I have an idea that in your heart of hearts you're a good Toad, and that you're sorry for all the trouble you've caused. Are you?
Toad (*off, inaudibly*) Yes, Badger.
Badger (*off, inaudibly*) In which case, though I should really lecture you for at least another half hour, are you repentant of your sins?

Toad (*off, inaudibly*) Yes, Badger. Truly, Badger.

Badger (*off, inaudibly*) Then we forgive you, Oh, Toad, Toad, are you really sorry?

Toad (*off, inaudibly*) Yes, Badger.

Ratty and Mole have been listening to this exchange, their heads cocked on one side, and now nod approvingly to each other

Badger and Toad enter. Toad is looking deflated

Badger My friends, I am pleased to inform you that Toad has seen the error of his ways. He is truly sorry for his misguided conduct, and he is going to forget all about motor cars for ever and ever.

Toad (*piously*) Amen.

Mole (*gravely*) This is very good news Toad.

Ratty (*dubiously*) Very good news—but where's the guarantee?

Badger Oh, I'll soon make him swear to it—that's no problem. Toad, tell them what you've just told me. That you're sorry for what you've done in the past; that you'll never do it again in the future, and that you see the folly of your ways.

There is a silence

Toad (*with sudden defiance*) No, I'm *not* sorry! And it wasn't folly at all! It was simply glorious!

Badger What? You backsliding animal! Didn't you tell me just now, over there, that . . .

Toad (*impatiently*) Oh yes, yes, *over there.* I'd have said anything *over there.* But over here I find that I'm not a bit sorry really, so it's no earthly good saying I am, now is it?

Badger Then you *don't* promise never to touch a motor car?

Toad Certainly not! On the contrary, I faithfully promise that the very first motor car I see—poop, poop!—off I go!

Ratty (*to Mole*) Told you so, didn't I?

Mole (*with a deep sigh*) Yes, Ratty.

Badger Very well. You can stew in your own juice. We three *civilized* animals are going for a walk now.

Ratty I've got a picnic waiting! I'd forgotten all about it! We'll spend the next hour eating and then I'll row you both up the river!

Mole (*jumping in the air with pleasure*) Oh my! Oh my! Oh my!

Badger (*to Toad*) You see what happens to *good* animals as compared to bad? *We* are going for a picnic but *you* will stay here and mull over your mistakes. When we come back we shall be expecting a reformed character.

Toad Well, you won't get one! Besides *I* like picnics! (*Greedily*) All that food . . . yum yum . . . (*He sticks his tongue out and swishes it from side to side of his mouth*)

Badger What you need is food for *thought.* I want you to sit down and think about the error of your ways.

Toad (*subdued*) Yes, Badger. I'll do that, Badger. And I humbly apologize for the trouble I'm causing.

Ratty I don't trust him, Badger. I've seen Toad being humble before. He isn't the least bit humble.

Badger In that case, Mole and I will go for a walk along the Riverbank and you must watch over Toad.

Toad (*with huge innocence*) I'll be good as gold.

Badger (*with a doubting look at Toad*) Guard him very carefully. Keep him out of mischief.

Ratty (*grimly*) I will Badger, don't you worry, I'll watch out for storms at sea.

Badger We'll have the picnic later. Is that in order Mole?

Mole Oh yes, Badger, anything's all right by me.

Badger Then come for a walk. We'll discuss *burrowing*.

Mole (*delightedly*) Burrowing? Oh my! Oh my! Oh my!

Badger makes burrowing gestures, Mole nods in agreement, and both exit

Toad sits on the tree trunk

Ratty (*pacing to and fro, hands behind his back*) I don't like having to guard you like this, Toad. You're my friend and it doesn't seem right.

Toad begins to act a dramatic illness scene

Toad (*tragically moaning*) Oooooh.

Ratty But if you're left alone, you'll only get up to some foolish prank, so I'm guarding you for your own good—do you understand?

Toad moans again and puts his hand to his head dramatically. Ratty continues pacing to and fro

It's hateful having to lecture you like this, but what can I do?

Toad (*swaying from side to side and moaning*) Oooooooh. . . .

Ratty (*concerned*) Now jump up and show a leg, there's a good fellow, and don't sit there moping like that!

Toad (*huskily*) Dear, kind Ratty . . . You don't realize how far—how very far—I am from "jumping up" and "showing a leg".

Ratty You've been a great burden to Badger, Mole and me.

Toad (*huskily*) I hate being a burden to my friends . . . (*Fatalistically*) . . . but I don't expect to be one much longer.

Ratty (*heartily*) Well, I hope not, too!

Toad I'm a nuisance, I know I am. . . .

Ratty You are indeed. But if only you'd be a sensible animal, I'd do anything on earth for you, it would be no trouble.

Toad In that case Ratty, I beg you—for the last time probably—to run down to the village—even now it may be too late—and fetch a doctor.

Ratty (*concerned now*) Fetch a doctor?

Toad No. Don't bother. It's only a trouble. Forget that I asked. (*He gives a loud groan and falls to the ground*) Oooooooh . . .

Ratty (*staring at Toad; alarmed*) Look here shipmate, of course I'll fetch a doctor for you, if you really think you need one. (*Suspiciously*) But why are you taken ill all of a sudden?

Toad (*ignoring this*) Er . . . by the way, while you're about it—I happen to remember that you pass his door on the way to the doctor—would you mind asking the *lawyer* to step round as well?

Ratty (*to the Audience*) The lawyer? I've never heard him ask for a lawyer before! He must be really bad! (*He looks offstage*) I'd like to consult with Mole and Badger, but they're far away by now . . . (*To the Audience*) I'd better humour Toad. (*To Toad*) Don't worry old fellow, I'll go to the doctor later.

Toad (*with great drama*) Oooooh . . .

Ratty I'd better go to the doctor *now*! (*With a farewell look at Toad*) Poor Toady . . . I'd better go fast!

Ratty exits

Toad looks about, furtively checking, then jumps up and joyously leaps about all over the place

Toad He's gone! I'm free! Now to put on my beautiful motoring coat again! Yes, now to *change gear*! Har, har, har! (*He runs to the pile of motoring clothing and starts to put them on*) Back to Toad Hall! And back to mankind's greatest marvel—the motor car! (*He starts to sing his Toad Song, as he climbs into the clothes*)

During this there is a loud sound effect of a period car engine chugging, with percussion effects, and, downstage, a cut-out of a 1908 jalopy/automobile is pushed onstage

Toad hears the engine noises, reacts, and exits into the wings with his motoring gear, but peers out to watch

A man and a woman, Fiona and Reginald, are behind the cut-out of the car, he is "turning" the driving wheel. Both wear period motoring clothes—he with a cap and goggles and she with a very big hat and motoring veil

Toad (*to the Audience, in a positive fever*) Good gracious! Good heavens! In fact, poop poop! Is it a Rolls Royce? Is it a Ford? Oh, the excitement! Oh, poop, poop!

Mainly in the wings, Toad puts on cap and gloves as he watches. The sound effects of the engine continue as Fiona gazes round

Fiona Reginald, why have you driven the car off the main road?

Reginald Because I've got something interesting to say to you, dearest.

Fiona (*looking around*) It's such a pretty place, I don't think anyone has ever been here before!

Reginald I'm not interested in the place, I'm interested in *you*.

Fiona (*pleased*) Reginald.

Reginald Dearest. Let me say what I want to say.

They gaze at each other romantically, the loud car noise effects stop

Oh. Bother the car. Excuse me. (*He comes round jauntily and athletically from behind the cut-out, pushing his goggles up. He holds up his forefinger coyly*) Won't be a jiffy! I'll turn the starting handle.

He bends down and mimes turning the starting handle. The car engine sound effects start again loudly and he runs back behind the cut-out again, and is thus once more "in the car"

There!

Fiona Well done! You were about to say something interesting to me, Reginald. . . .

Reginald Yes, I was dearest. I was going to say that of all the girls I've ever known, you're the only one who—well—who—who—

They gaze at each other romantically, but the car noises stop again

Oh. Bother the car. Excuse me. (*He runs round from the cut-out and takes a spanner from his coat pocket*) Won't be a jiffy! It must be something to do with the underneath. (*He lies on the floor in front of the car, and "fixes" some part of it*)

Fiona The "underneath"? I don't think you know the first thing about automobiles, Reginald.

Reginald (*calling*) I don't dearest.

Fiona Then for Pete's sake, stand up and pour in some more petrol!

Reginald (*sitting up*) I haven't *got* any more petrol!

Fiona (*exasperated*) Oh *Reginald*! Then what shall we do?

Reginald We'll just have to walk to the garage that's nearest, dearest.

Fiona now comes from behind the cut-out

Fiona (*impatiently*) In that case, hurry up!

Reginald Won't be a jiffy!

Fiona Be quick Reginald. Follow me. (*She starts to exit*) And if you say "Won't be a jiffy" once more, I shall scream.

Reginald Sorry, dearest. Are you sure the car will be safe here?

Fiona In the middle of the countryside? Are you thinking someone might steal it, you idiot? Come *on*, Reginald.

Reginald Yes, dearest. Won't be a jiffy.

Fiona (*utterly exasperated*) Doh!

Fiona storms out and Reginald follows, meekly

Toad, now dressed in his motoring gear, rushes out and stands in front of the car

Toad (*holding his hands up in ecstasy*) Oh, poop poop! Poop poop! Now, where's the starting handle . . . I bet it'll start for *me*! (*He bends down and mimes turning the handle at the front of the car. The engine starts. He runs behind the cut-out where he "changes" gear*) Into reverse—that's it! Then off with the brake and we're away! Har, har, har!

The car is pulled back into the wings, Toad turning his head as though reversing. There is a loud, triumphant reprise of the music of Song 2

(*Calling out over the music and car sound effects; greatly happy*) Poop poop! Poop, poop! Oh poop tiddly oop poop, *poop, poop*!

Toad and the car exit

Fiona and Reginald run on and call out after Toad and the car

Fiona Come back! Thief! Thief!
Reginald You stole my car! I saw you!
Fiona It was a Toad, Reginald! Call for the police, Reginald!
Reginald Yes, dearest. (*Calling out fatuously*) Police! Police!
Fiona (*to the distant Toad*) Thief! Thief! Toad! Toad!
Reginald (*gazing round helplessly*) Police! Police!

Black-out

Scene 2

The Corridor leading to the Courtroom

A frontcloth is flown in or the Tabs are closed, there is a fanfare and, either from the Auditorium or from the wings, a solemn procession enters to the music of Song 4(A)

The entire cast enter beginning with the Clerk of the Court, several depressed Rabbits who shake their heads sadly, then several cockily triumphant Weasels, then the Chief Weasel clasping his hands above his head like a victorious boxer. The Magistrate follows, then the unhappy Mole, Ratty and Badger, shaking their heads, followed by Reginald and Fiona. The Policeman brings up the rear, escorting Toad who is still in motoring gear but now wearing very large handcuffs and looking doleful

Everyone sings

Song 4(A): Short parody from "Iolanthe"

All   Bow, bow, ye lower middle classes!
                                  Bow, bow, ye peasants, bow ye masses!
                                  Blow the trumpet, bang the brasses!
                                  Tantantara! Tzing! Boom!

The Magistrate steps forward and sings

Magistrate   I'm a peer of highest station
                                  Paragon of Legislation
                                  Pillar of the British nation.
All   Tantantara! Tzing! Boom!

The Clerk of the Court rings his hand bell

Clerk (*proclaiming*) First case to be tried today is Toad versus the Crown—
are all the Jury present?
Rabbits
Weasels } (*together*) Yes!
Clerk Nobody missing?

Rabbits } (*together*) No!
Weasels }

Toad (*mournfully*) I wish I was ...

Policeman Quiet, you. Carry on, Mr Clerk!

Clerk (*proclaiming*) To be held at the Courtroom of the Castle, the case of Toad versus the Crown, Mr Toad having stolen a motor car from the Riverbank and later crashed it on the King's Highway—

Badger (*groaning loudly*) Oh, helpless Toad! Oh, hapless animal! I knew his father, I knew his grandfather, I knew ...

All QUIET!

Clerk (*nodding to the Magistrate*) Your Lordship.

All listen to the Magistrate as he sings, or talks, with comical hatred the short parody from The Mikado. *Before starting he takes from up his sleeve a huge piece of parchment which he unrolls, this being his "list"*

Song 4(B)

Magistrate	I've got a little secret And it's one I cannot hide I've got a little list
All	He's got a little list
Magistrate	On people that I hate and who I'm going to put inside And who never would be missed
All	Who never would be missed.
Magistrate	There are nasty little boys and girls Who only want to shock Who stand there in the witness box And call out "Wotcher cock" Or the green haired girl in leather Who just stands there chewing gum And when I'm summing up the case She shouts out "Gee! You're dumb!" And when I tell her "Silence" She just waves a threatening fist I don't think she'd be missed I'm *sure* she'd not be missed.
All	He's got 'em on the list He's got 'em on the list And they'd none of them be missed They'd none of them be missed.
Magistrate	I get a lot of *animals* That come here to be tried I've got a little list
All	He's got a little list
Magistrate	There are foxes, hedgehogs, squirrels And some other ones beside They never would be missed
All	They never would be missed

Magistrate	There are dogs who bark and jump about
	And once we had a pig
	I recall we had an ostrich
	And it ate my Judge's wig
	Then one day I had to try a *snake*
	You could have knocked me flat
	But when the snake was sentenced
	I said "Wriggle out of that!"
	And the animals I hate the most
	Are toads—and I insist
	They'd none of them be missed
	They'd none of them be missed
All	He's got 'em on the list
	He's got 'em on the list
	And they'd none of them be missed
	They'd none of them be missed!
Magistrate	So bow, bow, ye lower middle classes
	Bow, bow, ye peasants, bow ye masses

All mime blowing trumpets and banging cymbals as they sing

All	Tarantara! Tzing! Boom!

The Tabs open to reveal

SCENE 3

The Court room at the Castle

There are two benches for the Jury, a cut-out of a Judge's desk, a cut-out of a witness box and perhaps the prison cell/dungeon grille placed in the permanent set. (See scenery notes)

The Magistrate goes up behind his desk and, by the final note of the song, all are in their respective places—the Jury standing at their benches, the Clerk and Policeman near the Magistrate and Toad at the witness box

All	Blow the trumpets, bang the brasses
	Tarantara!
	Tarantara!
	Tarantara!—Tzing—Boom!

On the "Boom" all sit and the Magistrate addresses them

Magistrate (*cheerfully*) I'm the Chairman of the Board of Magistrates. Everybody sit down—oh, you have done. In that case, put your feet up and make yourselves at home—(*with great emphasis*)—except for Toad, who I've already decided is guilty.

One of the Weasels steps forward, both hands held up like a dog begging, and hops across the stage on both feet

What's he doing?
Clerk He thinks it's a kangaroo court.

Everyone laughs as the Weasel is pulled back to the Jury bench by the Chief Weasel

Magistrate Toad, you're guilty as the nose on my face, but what have you got to say in your defence? You were down by the Riverbank, and what did you see from there?

Toad has been very subdued but now steps forward from the witness box

Toad (*politely*) My Lord, a beautiful car was driven into the area.
Magistrate For what reason?
Toad I think the original reason was Romance—but something went a bit wrong.

Everyone laughs noisily

Magistrate "Went a bit wrong?" *What* went a bit wrong?
Toad Well, my Lord, it was like this. (*He steps forward and sings*)

Song 5

Linking vamp music continues as the Magistrate steps forward from his desk

Magistrate How very singular! (*He sings, extremely jazzily for a Magistrate and "out of character"*)

Song 5 (reprise)

When the Magistrate has sung eight bars, everyone starts to leave their places and join him. Then for a third chorus all go into a:

Production Routine

After the ragtime song and dance, the music fades and all return to their places, the Magistrate being the first to return. The Clerk rings his bell a couple of times

Magistrate Well, Mr Toad, that's the evidence according to you. According to *me* Toad stole a valuable motor car, didn't he Jury?
Weasels (*loudly*) Yes!
Rabbits, Mole } (*together;* } No!
Ratty and Badger } *indignantly*) }
Magistrate And Toad drove it to the public danger and he crashed it, didn't he Jury?
Weasels Yes!
Rabbits, Mole } (*together;* } NO!
Ratty and Badger } *fed up*) }
Magistrate (*to the Audience*) Oh I *am* enjoying this. He's so obviously guilty! And he was grossly impertinent to the local police, wasn't he Constable?

The Police Constable steps forward and takes the stage. He coughs and does the traditional policeman's knees bend, fingers tucked into his belt, and addresses the Audience. He is obviously going to make a speech of tremendous importance

Policeman Yus.

Magistrate (*briskly*) Then Clerk of the Court, what is the stiffest punishment we can impose?

Clerk I have it worked out me lud. (*He holds up some paper, peers at it and reads out*) "A pound of potatoes, a tin of grapefruit, a lettuce, six eggs. ..."

The Weasels laugh heartily but Toad, Ratty, Mole and Badger look angry

(*Turning over the paper*) Ah! Supposing we say ... (*Loudly*) Twelve months for the theft of the car ...

Magistrate That's a mild sentence, isn't it?

Weasels (*very loudly; confidently*) YES!

Rabbits, Badger, } (*together;* No!
Mole and Ratty } *defiantly*)

Clerk (*loudly*) Four years for the furious driving ...

Magistrate That's a lenient sentence, isn't it?

Weasels (*loudly and confidently*) YES!

Rabbits, Badger, } (*together*) No!
Mole and Ratty }

Clerk (*loudly*) And fifteen years for cheeking the Police ...

Magistrate That's a first rate sentence, isn't it?

Weasels Yes!

Rabbits, Badger, } (*together*) No!
Mole and Ratty }

Magistrate Then Jury, is Toad guilty or not guilty?

The Weasels and Ferrets stand up

Weasels } (*together;* } Guil-tee! Guil-tee! Guil-tee! Guil-tee!
Ferrets } *chanting*) }

They sit down again, as Ratty, Mole and Badger stand up from their bench

Ratty, Mole and Badger Oh no he's not! (*They sit down again*)

Weasels (*standing up and shouting*) Oh yes, he is! (*They sit again*)

Ratty, Mole and Badger (*standing up*) Oh no, he's not! (*They remain standing*)

Weasels (*standing up*) Oh yes, he is! (*They remain standing*)

Ratty, Mole and Badger Oh no, he's ...

The Clerk and Policeman watch in shocked amazement. The Magistrate blows a whistle taken from his pocket, and holds up a yellow card, football-referee-style. Grumbling to each other, everyone sits down

Magistrate You're all impertinent! I'm the Judge, so I'll do the judging! Toad, I've listened carefully to the Jury and this time the sentence is twenty years.

Weasels (*waving their arms frenetically*) 'Oooooooray!

Ratty, Mole, Badger and the Rabbits shake their heads miserably. Toad is subdued and tragic

Magistrate (*to all*) You've heard of the dismal dungeon they call "The Hole"?

All Yes!

Magistrate Put him in there.

Toad No!

Magistrate He's guilty, so . . . (*Loudly commanding to the Policeman and the Clerk*) Toad in the Hole!

Weasels (*loudly*) Toad in the 'ole! 'Ooooooooray!!

The music, 4(A), is reprised as at the opening of the scene

The Policeman takes Toad and marches him downstage and then in a circle round and up into the area of the dungeon grille

At the same time, everyone stands up when the Magistrate does, and as they sing, 4A (reprise) they form the procession again and march round the stage. The Weasels laugh, but all the Friends of Toad shake their heads gloomily

Song 4(A) (reprise)

All   Bow, bow, ye lower middle classes
                          Bow, bow, ye peasants, bow ye masses
                          Blow the trumpet, bang the brasses
                          Tantantara!
                          Tantantara!—Tzing—Boom!

Everyone exits, except Toad

Toad sits on one of the Jury benches or a tree trunk that is now in front of the dungeon grille that has a practical door to it (See Scenery notes)

SCENE 3(B)

The Hole—a dungeon in the Castle

Toad is alone on stage

Toad (*with a pathetic attempt at defiance*) I am Toad! The handsome, the popular, the successful—Oh, oh, oh. (*He breaks down into genuine tears and sobs*) This is the end of everything—or rather it's the end of Toad, which is the same thing! How can I *ever* hope to be free after stealing that car in such a cheeky manner! Stupid animal that I am! I'll never eat again, never, never, never, not even bread and water! Oh! (*He gazes at the floor despondently*)

In the Courtroom area, the Policeman enters with a pretty girl, Jenny, his daughter, in a country dress, who carries a bowl and spoon

Policeman Jenny, stop botherin' me. Toad's trial has made me quite fatigued. I don't think I can cope any more.

Jenny But, father, you know 'ow fond of animals I am! I've got a pet mouse, a pet squirrel *and* a pet canary, so why can't I 'ave a pet Toad?

Policeman I'm sick and tired of Toad. You can do what you like with 'im. I'm goin' downstairs for a cuppa tea. (*He hands her the huge bunch of keys hooked on to his belt*) You look after 'im, I know I can trust you.

Jenny (*kissing him*) Thanks, Dad.

Jenny sings happily to herself as she crosses the Courtroom area to behind the dungeon door, mimes she is unlocking it, enters the dungeon area, and mimes locking the door again

Meanwhile the Policeman addresses the Audience

Policeman This Courtroom and Dungeon is very old, you know. I've heard it said as 'ow we 'ad Dick Turpin 'ere for a stretch—and Doctor Crippen—and Jack The Ripper. (*Screwing up his face, about to weep*) They was nuffink as compared to Toad. Well, whoever heard of a Policeman being ordered to frog-march a frog? It don't make sense, do it? (*Calling off; a bit desperately*) Mavis, is that cuppa tea ready? If I don't 'ave a cuppa tea soon, I'll explode!

Policeman exits

Jenny Now cheer up, Toad! I'm Jenny the Policeman's daughter!

Toad Well, that won't cheer me up will it?

Jenny No, but this might. It's some of my dinner, it's hot from the oven.

Toad I'll never eat again! Never, never, never! (*Greatly curious*) What is it?

Jenny Bubble and squeak.

Toad Out of the question. It's far too common.

Jenny Well, it's that or bread and water.

Toad Bread and wa ...? (*He grabs the bowl from her and gobbles its contents, making a great clatter with the spoon and with his eating*)

Jenny (*laughing as she takes the bowl from him*) I thought you said it was far too common?

Toad It is! See here, my girl, we don't serve bubble and squeak at Toad Hall! (*Grandly*) I *own* Toad Hall you know.

Jenny Really? Is it a hotel?

Toad stands up and paces about

Toad No—it is *not* an hotel. (*Emotionally; not conceitedly*) It's an Elizabethan Manor, with Elizabethan library, Elizabethan banqueting room, Elizabethan kitchen.

Jenny (*impressed*) Fancy!

Toad And the telephone's hidden in a suit of armour—my idea of course. And in the stables there's a wash-house, and there's a ...

Jenny (*with much interest*) A real wash-house?

Toad (*surprised*) Yes. I think so. Why are you so interested in a wash-house? I was telling you about the stables—my family's famous for its horse riders you know.

Jenny My family's famous for its washerwomen.

Toad Pardon?

Jenny We're *all* washerwomen! My mother takes in washing in the town and my Aunties do all the washing 'ere in the prison.

Toad The washing for the whole prison?

Jenny nods

Just how many Aunts have you got?

Jenny Six. You should see 'em with a prisoner's underpants in one 'and and a packet of soap powder in the other! Then they scrubs and scrubs—it's like poetry in motion!

Toad stands still now

Toad (*dreamily*) I once said that about a motor car I'd stolen. I know I *shouldn't* have stolen it—I couldn't help it—it was beautiful.

Jenny I like you, Toady. And I feel really sorry for you. (*Shocked*) Twenty years for stealing a motor car! (*She looks thoughtful*)

Toad (*starting to cry*) Look at me! I was once the handsome Toad, the happy Toad, the *hospitable* Toad! But now how can I ever hope to see the blue sky again?

Jenny Toad, my Aunt Nellie takes out the washing from this place on Monday, and brings it back on a Friday. (*Emphasizing*) *This is Friday!*

Toad I don't quite follow.

Jenny Well, this is what occurs to me. My Dad's already told me that you're rich—and my Aunty Nellie's poor. For a few pounds she'd let you 'ave 'er dress and bonnet and stuff, and you could escape from the castle disguised!

Toad What? You're mad!

Jenny If six of my Aunts comes in, no one's going to notice if one of 'em goes out a bit green in the gills!

Toad *Green in the gills?* You're being extremely cheeky. And you surely wouldn't have Mr Toad, of Toad Hall, going about the countryside disguised as a *washerwoman*?

Jenny Why not? My Aunties will soon be leaving the prison—they 'ave to pass your door—I wonder if I can catch 'em before they leaves?

Raucous laughter is heard off

(*Excitedly*) That's them now! Will you trust me?

Toad You're the only one I *can* trust!

Jenny Then three pounds for Auntie. (*She cheekily holds out her hand*)

Toad Delighted! (*He gives the money to her*)

Jenny runs up to the door, unlocks it and looks out

Jenny (*calling off*) Is that you Auntie? Auntie Nellie! Yooo—hoo! Aunties—are you there?

Music, and the six Edwardian Cockney washerwomen enter laughing and chatting. They wear black bonnets, shawls and sport ostrich feathers in their hats

Nellie So I said to 'im, "Keep yer 'ands to yerself, Billy Lampton, or I'll give yer a bit of what for!"

All six laugh raucously and then stop laughing when they see Toad

Jenny Aunties, this is my friend Toad. Toad, this is Auntie Nellie ...
Nellie Pleased to meet you, I'm sure!

Nellie gives a quick curtsy. Toad bows his head, very much the gentleman

Jenny Auntie Maggie ...
Maggie Nice to make your acquaintance Mr Toad!

Maggie gives a quick curtsy, Toad bows back

Jenny Auntie Flo ...
Flo Hullo dearie! Don't look so down in the dumps

Flo curtsies, Toad solemnly bows

Jenny Auntie Patsy ...
Patsy Arternoon, Mr Toad! (*She curtsies*)

Toad bows to Patsy

Jenny Auntie Clementina.

Clementina moves forward graciously and holds out her hand

Clementina Everso pleased to meet you, Mr Frog.

Toad reacts

And I do hope as you are well and everythink?

Clementina and Toad shake hands

Jenny Auntie Nellie—you want to make a few quid on the side? (*She holds the notes up*)
Nellie (*thrilled, taking them*) Ooooooh yes! (*To Toad*) I'm that skint dearie! Stoneybroke, as the saying is. (*To Jenny*) Wot do I 'ave to do dear?
Jenny We've got to move fast, before me Dad comes back. We'll nip into the next cell and I'll explain everythink to you.
Nellie Oh! I can't wait! (*To Toad*) Excitin' ain't it?
Toad (*apprehensively*) I'm not sure. I've never been a washerwoman before.
Nellie (*surprised*) What you going to be a washerwoman for? 'Ow very peculiar!

As Jenny, Toad and Aunt Nellie exit the five washerwomen let out an unfeeling laugh

Maggie I don't know why I'm laughin', I've got such a lot on me mind.
Flo Yes, Maggie, what's all this about movin' 'ouse?
Maggie Well dear, I'm leavin' the prison early today so I can get back 'ome and get organized *proper* this time. I don't want none of the trouble like wot I 'ad last time I moved.
Clementina What 'appened, Maggie?

Maggie Well my old man, 'e gave me careful instructions and like a fool, I . . . well, I'll tell you about it dear.

Maggie sings and the other washerwomen gather round her, nodding with interest as she tells them her tale of woe

Song 6

Production Routine

All five raucously reprise the chorus into the Cockney knees up, and they move on to a quick version of "Knees Up Mother Brown" to end the routine

After the production number Jenny enters

Jenny Aunties, I'm sorry I 'ad to leave you but I 'ad to help poor Mr Toad. He should never have been insinuated in a dungeon like this, now should 'e?
Aunts No—you're quite right dear—it's true!
Jenny He's innocent—*nearly*—so I've taken the law into me own 'ands.
Maggie (*alarmed*) What d'you mean dear?
Jenny Well, to start with, 'ere's wot's 'appened to Auntie Nellie!

There is a quick fanfare, and Auntie Nellie enters in period underwear with hand-cuffs on her wrists, and many chains and ropes dangling and trailing along the ground. She has a gag tied over her mouth

Everyone laughs

That's what "that unutterable cad, Mr Toad" is supposed to 'ave done to 'er.

Everyone laughs again

No one'll ever guess she was the one wot *helped* 'im to escape, now will they?
Maggie Never!
Flo Jenny, you are a scream and no mistake!
Patsy (*with great admiration*) Such *cheek*!
Jenny Oh, I forgot—'ere's my *new* Auntie!

There is a grand fanfare as Toad enters as a magnificent period cockney washerwoman/flower seller type

Toad (*waving triumphantly*) Hullo, Ladies! Oh this is splendid! Simply splendid! (*Remembering*) Oh . . . (*attempting some Cockney*) Wotcher cock! I'll soon be darn the old apples and pears and 'art of the rorie o'moore.
Jenny Rorie o'moore?
All Door!

Everyone laughs again, enjoying the situation

Music starts—Song 6 played Elgar style, a slow and grandiose tempo. Toad stands centre stage, a somewhat odd looking heroic figure

Toad (*over the music*) I want to thank Aunt Nellie, and dear Jenny, and all you splendid ladies for you help. When I'm back in circulation, you must all come and stay with me at dear old Toad Hall for the longest holiday you've ever had!
All (*delighted*) 'Oooooray!
Toad You deserve it!

During the following, the washerwomen get down on one knee at each side of Toad, humming the grandiose sounding slow reprise of song 6 to "Aaaaah"

(*Dramatically*) But now to more serious matters. The Chief Weasel wants me out of the way so that he can terrorize the neighbourhood! But we must have freedom and justice along the Riverbank! So somehow I must fight the Chief Weasel and somehow I must win! Once again, thank you for your help, Ladies, thank you. I'm free!!! (*With a grand gesture and pose*) Back to the Riverbank!
Jenny \ (*together; quite* \| Goodbye Toad! Good luck dear! Ta, ta ducks! Bye
Aunts \| *carried away*) \| bye! You give 'em what for!

Toad the washerwoman strides up to the open dungeon door and magnificently waves goodbye to the Ladies and to the Audience. There is a loud fanfare and:

Tableau

CURTAIN

Note: Fewer aunts can be used, or if the scene is to consist of only Toad, Jenny and one aunt (Nellie) then it is as follows

Jenny runs up to the dungeon door, unlocks it and looks out

Jenny (*calling off*) Is that you Auntie? Auntie Nellie! Yoooo—hooo!

Aunt Nellie enters

Nellie 'Ello dear!
Jenny Auntie, this is my friend Toad. Toad, this is Auntie Nellie.
Nellie Pleased to meet you I'm sure! (*She gives a quick curtsy*)
Toad Charmed. (*He solemnly bows his head*)
Jenny Aunt Nellie—you want to make a few quid on the side? (*She holds up the money*)
Nellie (*thrilled; taking the notes*) Oooooh yes! (*To Toad*) I'm that skint dearie! Stoneybroke, as the saying is! (*To Jenny*) Wot do I 'ave to do dear?
Jenny Take your clothes off.
Nellie Pardon?
Toad Madam, if you could help a gentleman who is in dire straits, I would be eternally grateful.
Nellie Yes dear, but why do I 'ave to take me clothes orf?
Jenny You have to look as though that unutterable cad Mr Toad has grabbed hold of you, taken your clothes, and escaped in them.
Nellie (*enthusiastically*) Oh! I can't wait! I've 'ad ever such a dull week so far. (*To Toad*) Excitin', ain't it?

Toad (*apprehensively*) I'm not sure. I've never been a washerwoman before.
Jenny Well, now's your chance to start! Come on, you two!

The cockney music of Song 6 is played loudly and Jenny claps in time and gets the Audience to clap along with her

While this happens, Nellie is feverishly removing her bonnet, shawl with safety pin, and full length black skirt. Toad is removing his coat, revealing green shirt, green short trousers and green tights. He collects the items from Auntie and feverishly puts on the bonnet, skirt, and safety-pins the shawl into position, maybe with Auntie's help. At exactly the same time as the music ends, so Toad and Auntie Nellie pose. Toad is now dressed as a washerwoman and Auntie is in Edwardian underwear, perhaps with a laced corset

(*Applauding the result*) Beautiful! But Mr Toad is supposed to have tied you up and shown you no mercy—so where's the rope?

Jenny looks round, sees some in the wings and collects two pieces

Toad (*indignantly looking at his new clothes*) The Great Toad, reduced to this!
Jenny Don't you dare complain, you ungrateful animal.
Toad I don't like it.
Jenny Then you can stop 'ere, in this dungeon. (*She puts the rope around Nellie*)
Toad (*hastily*) You're quite right. You're a good and clever girl and I'm a proud and stupid toad. My apologies.

Nellie holds her wrists behind her and Jenny wraps the rope round them. Toad takes the other piece of rope and drapes it round Nellie's neck and waist

Nellie (*as she is roped up*) Aren't you going to gag me? You must gag me dear. We must be authentic. I mean, I must look pillaged and ravaged, now, mustn't I?
Jenny I'll use me hankie. Sit down, Auntie.

Nellie sits on the log or bench while Jenny gags her. Toad shows off his washerwoman disguise

Toad (*displaying himself*) How do I look?
Jenny What d'you think Auntie?

Gagged, Nellie nods vigorously and makes enthusiastic noises

Toad (*formally*) Then the time has come for me to register my gratitude to you, ladies. When I'm back in circulation, you must come and stay with me at dear old Toad Hall for the longest holiday you've ever had!
Jenny We'd like that—wouldn't we Auntie?

Nellie nods and gurgles enthusiastically

Toad But now for more serious matters ...

Song 6 music is now played at a grandiose Elgar style tempo as Toad addresses the Audience, a mixture of a hero and Charley's Aunt

The Chief Weasel wants me out of the way so that he can terrorize the neighbourhood! But we must have freedom and justice along the River-bank! So somehow I must fight the Chief Weasel and somehow I must win! Once again, Ladies, thank you for your help—I'm free!!! (*With a grand gesture as he poses at the open dungeon door*) Back to the Riverbank!

Jenny (*waving emotionally*) Goodbye Toad—I shall miss you—good luck!

Toad waves back, the music becomes a fanfare

Tableau

CURTAIN

ACT II

The canal bank near the Castle

The permanent set of countryside and trees. Perhaps there is a cut-out of a barge behind the upstage groundrow that now represents a canal bank. See scenery notes

Song 7

The Friendly Animals, plus their offspring, sing and dance—it's a country square dance or a 1908 "Bunny Hug" ragtime routine

After the song they chatter to each other with animated paw gestures, Mrs Otter and Portly being downstage

Mrs Otter Come on, Portly, we'll go and swim in the river now.
Portly (*disappointed*) Oh *Mum.* Can't I stay here and play?
Mrs Otter Certainly not! The Chief Weasel might get you!
Portly But the Wild Wood's a long way off!
Mrs Otter I know it is, dear, but that Weasel's such a crafty creature, he wants to take over the whole countryside. (*To the others*) Isn't that the truth?
All Yes, Mrs Otter!
Mrs Otter He wants to *rule* over us animals—and I think he's going to, don't you?
All That's right, Mrs Otter!
1st Rabbit (*dramatically*) You see Portly, there's no one strong enough to stop him. We animals need a leader, but we haven't got one, have we?
Portly (*importantly; shaking his head*) No. We haven't got a leader.
1st Rabbit So none of us is safe.
All (*with concern*) We're worried! We're in danger!
Portly (*to 1st Rabbit*) Then shall I go swimming with Mum?
1st Rabbit *Yes,* Portly.
Portly (*taking Mrs Otter's hand*) I'll go swimming after all, Mum.

Mrs Otter and Portly start to exit, the other animal families following

   The Bargewoman enters and calls to them

Bargewoman Ay! Me dears! Afore you go, any of you as wants some washin' done?

The animals turn back

I've me barge over there on the canal, and me washtub's in the barge.

Mrs Otter What a good idea! All Mr Otter's shirts want doing, and I don't know how many things of Portly's. How much is a family wash?

Bargewoman Sixpence.

Animals (*looking at each other with delight*) Sixpence?

Bargewoman That's all me dears. So you collects yer washin' and I'll collects me washtub!

Animals (*variously*) Sixpence!
 What a bargain!
 Come and collect the wash, Henry!
 Only sixpence a wash!

The chattering Rabbits exit one side and the Bargewoman exits the other

As they go, there is dramatic music, the Lights darken and a green spot picks up the Chief Weasel as he swaggers in holding an open map

Chief Weasel (*to the audience*) Huh! I heard those stupid animals chattering. So the little dears want a leader do they? A hero to protect them from horrible me! But they aren't going to find one, 'cos Toad's *in prison* isn't he?

Audience No! (*etc*)

Chief Weasel Silence! If I say he is, he is! (*He checks the map*) Now, this is the canal bank that leads on to the Riverbank, then it leads on to Toad Hall. What a delightful part of the world—and who's going to stop me taking it over? Nobody. You've only got to mention the words "Chief Weasel" and everyone trembles with terror! (*He leers at the Audience*) I was born to frighten my fellow animals, and I'm awfully good at it. (*He starts to exit but turns back as though he has heard some audience reaction, which he probably will have done*) I heard that! Don't answer me back, or I'll be down there amongst you, wreaking havoc—and that's not a pretty sight, believe me. (*Sneering*) Huh, you're not even rabbits—you're *humans*!

He swaggers off

The daylight returns, and the Bargewoman enters with her washtub (on wheels or legs) and holding the rope halter to which Dobbin is tied, he entering with her

Bargewoman (*dumping down the washtub*) Come on! You be a real ole nag, bain't you?

Dobbin shakes his head

You better have some sugar, 'cos sugar is energy. (*She takes some sugar from her pocket and holds it to Dobbin's mouth*) And you be goin' to need energy, as you goin' ter pull my barge fer six hours now. Aye—six hours without a stop. (*Sarcastically*) You'll enjoy that, won't you?

Dobbin mournfully shakes his head

We just passed the Castle and we got to reach Rookham by evenin'. (*She *takes the rope and hits Dobbin*) You go and graze in that there field whiles you got the chance! (*With sarcasm*) So you used to pull a *lovely luxury* caravan, did 'ee?

Dobbin nods

And Mr Toad was *nice* to 'ee, was 'ee?

Dobbin nods

Well, now you're pullin' a ten ton barge so don't get no fancy ideas about *me* bein' nice. (*She hits him with the rope again*) Go on, off you go, you four-legged old fool!

With head lowered, Dobbin exits sadly to mournful music

Toad enters from the other side, still disguised as a washerwoman. He is running and looks flustered and glances back over his shoulder

Toad (*exhausted*) Oh! Oh! Am I being followed? No. Thank goodness for that.

Still looking offstage he bustles onwards and crashes into the Bargewoman who is looking off after Dobbin

Bargewoman (*aggressively*) That's my rheumaticky arm! (*She sees Toad and becomes all charm*) Well! A nice morning, ma'am! Be you one of us, dear?
Toad One of us?
Bargewoman Yes, luv. A bargewoman. (*She nudges him hard with her elbow*) Understand?
Toad No ... no ... (*Remembering*) I'm a *washer*woman. (*He nudges her back hard*) Understand?

The Bargewoman, unsure, looks Toad up and down

(*His nerves taking over*) Yes, and I *love* it! (*He pushes up both sleeves*) I simply dote on it! Washing, ironing, starching—oh, I'm never so happy as when I've got both me arms in the washtub back in London! I live in London you see. I'm a Cockney. (*With a dreadful accent*) Cor blimey.
Bargewoman You doesn't sound very Cockney to me dear. But maybe that's 'cos you be in such a pickle.
Toad (*giving a "character" performance*) Oh, pickle isn't the word for it! I'm in sore trouble and no mistake. It's me married daughter, ma'am. I'm in such a mad rush to reach me daughter, I'm all confused!
Bargewoman Where might your daughter be living, ma'am? (*She straightens her shawl and pats her hair*)
Toad In Toad Hall—I mean, near Toad Hall. (*He straightens his shawl in the same way, and pats his hair*)
Bargewoman Well, as it 'appens, I be goin' that way meself! (*Pointing off*) First we passes the Gypsy Camp, then we soon reaches Toad 'All. Tell you what me dear, you do a little job fer *me* (*She points to herself*) and I'll do a little job fer 'ee. (*She points to Toad*)
Toad (*apprehensively*) What "little job" will you do for me?

Bargewoman I'll take 'ee in the barge to Toad 'All.

Toad (*bursting out happily, scampering about and addressing the Audience*) Toad's in luck again! Toad always comes out on top! Har, har, har! Splendid, simply splendid! Oh Toad, Toad old chap, you *are* a card and no mistake! (*He suddenly remembers his Cockney character and stops still*) Ta everso much, duckie.

Bargewoman And in exchange you can do a little job for me.

Toad Delighted!

Bargewoman Do me washin'.

Toad (*airily*) Even more delighted! (*To the Audience*) Any old fool can wash! Har har har!

Mrs Otter, Portly and the other animals enter with huge piles of washing. The Bargewoman takes from the tub a huge packet of soap powder

Bargewoman Ah, here be the washin' then.

Toad sees all the washing and reacts with dismay

Toad What?

Bargewoman In goes the first pile, me dear! (*She takes a great pile from Little Portly, and calls*) Sixpence a wash! Sixpence a wash!

Toad (*aside; to the Audience, aghast*) I've never washed a thing in my life— not even a handkerchief!

Some of the animals, with Portly are pushing their washing into the tub, including sheets

Bargewoman Handkerchief? I might ask you to wash a sheet later.

Toad (*horrified*) A sheet? You mean one of those things that you put on a bed?

Bargewoman What d'you think you put them on—the floor? Come on, me dear, pour in the soap powder and get started!

Toad (*bluffing*) Er ... right! (*He rubs his hands together professionally, as though used to all this*)

Mrs Otter Which of you ladies do I give my sixpence to?

Bargewoman Me. (*She puts out her hand for it*)

Toad *Me.*

As Mrs Otter gives her coin to the Bargewoman, Toad snatches it

In fact, I'll collect all your sixpences if I may. (*As he quickly collects coins from each group*) Thank you, thank you, thank you, thank you. Well, that's the sixpences, so now for the wash! (*With great confidence, he holds up the large packet and pours powder into the tub. Airily chatting*) Nothing I like better than washing. I remember one day me daughter said to me, "Mum" she said, "I've seen some fine washerwomen in my day, but you take the biscuit. You've got such style, such finesse, and what's more you can do a wash quicker than anyone I've ever known." So I said to her, I said ...

Toad is pouring and pouring and pouring the powder into the tub. The Animals and the Bargewoman gather round to watch and become suspicious and exchange looks

Bargewoman 'Ere, what on earth be you doin'?

Toad Pouring!

Bargewoman Pourin'? You baint got the faintest idea how to do a wash, now 'ave you? (*She peers at him*) I don't believe you *are* a washerwoman, you old wind bag! Yes, that's what you are—a wind bag!

Toad (*loudly, all his motherly Cockney gone*) Don't you *dare* talk to me like that, you low, common, *fat*, bargewoman!

Bargewoman (*aghast*) What?

Toad Fancy even *thinking* that I was a washerwoman! I'll have you know I am a toad—a respected, well known and distinguished toad! I may be under a cloud at present, but all the same, *I am Toad!*

The animals turn to each other and react with surprise

Bargewoman (*amazed*) A toad? (*Peering at Toad, from head to toe*) Why so you be! You be a horrid, nasty, creepy, crawly toad!

Toad And you—I'll tell you what you be. You be a loud mouthed, ugly, rude, rustic load of rubbish.

Bargewoman You be a fraud, that's what you be! We want our money back, don't we everybody?

Animals Yes!

Toad You'll get the money when you get me! Which will be never!

Bargewoman After 'im!

Toad (*jumping in the air*) HELP!

Loud chase music (Song 8) as Toad runs down into the Auditorium, followed by the shouting Bargewoman, Mrs Otter and the other angry animals

Dobbin runs in, wondering what the noise is about

Mrs Otter (*in the auditorium*) Give me my sixpence!

Animals (*shouting*) Where's our money? We want our sixpences! It's disgraceful! We want our money back! After him—after him! The Toad! The Toad!

In the Auditorium, hotly pursued, Toad looks round wildly for an escape route and now sees Dobbin, who neighs with delight, "waves" from the stage, and jumps up and down

Toad (*from the Auditorium*) Dobbin! My dear old friend, you couldn't have come at a better time! (*Happily laughing*) Har, har, har!

Toad runs back on the stage, and kicks over the washtub. Dobbin neighs again, quickly lowers himself to allow Toad to climb on his back, and they both start to exit

Onwards—to Toad Hall! Tally ho, yoicks, tantivvy, and all that sort of thing! Tally ho! Tally ho! Tally ho!

Toad and Dobbin exit

Sound effects of a horse galloping are heard and the furious Bargewoman and shouting Animals return on stage

Bargewoman (*with an enraged shout*) Come back, Dobbin!

Mrs Otter (*shouting*) Come back, washerwoman! (*She picks up some washing and waves it angrily*)

Bargewoman (*shouting*) Come back, Toad! I'll put the Police on 'ee! I will, I'll call the Police, you sees if I doesn't! (*She also waves some washing in the air, angrily*)

All Come back Toad! Come back Toad! Come back Toad! (*They all chant and wave washing around above their heads*)

The sound effects of galloping continue briefly until

Black-out

At once, wild gypsy music is heard—a few bars of "Oh, Chechanya"

SCENE 2

The Gypsy Camp further along the Canal

Tabs or frontcloth of some caravans in a field with the canal nearby. (See scenery notes). Dim lighting and gypsy music

A few of the gypsies enter, prominent being Zelda, their wizened old leader. She has a stoop, an upside-down pipe in her mouth, and has in her ragged, dirty apron pocket some nasty black and green props later dealt with in detail. By her side stands a gypsy girl holding a cauldron or large saucepan

Only a few Gypsies need enter here—those people that were not animals in the previous scene—but this Gypsy scene ends with the Production Number that should include all the Chorus and small-part people

Zelda (*to Gypsies*) Zingaros! Gitani! Gypsies! (*Beckoning them closer, each side of her*) I've called you together and you understand that we're in great trouble?

The Gypsies wave their right arm

Gypsies Aye, Zelda! Romani Zingaros!

Zelda You will accept me as your leader—and will help me in this time of hardship?

Gypsies (*waving their right arms*) Sa Roma Prala! All gypsies are brothers!

Zelda We are but a poor, small, tribe. We go hop picking, we make clothes pegs, we tell fortunes. (*She holds out her gnarled hand towards the Audience*) Tell your fortune pretty lady? (*Disgustedly*) Pah! It doesn't earn us much mazooma, does it, my people?

Gypsies (*variously; shaking their heads*) No money!

Molto Charo!
Zateena!

1st Gypsy It's a bad time for us!

2nd Gypsy (*desperate*) We *must* earn some money Zelda!

3rd Gypsy Soon we shall be starvin'!

4th Gypsy What are we going to do, Zelda?

Gypsies Aye! What are we going to do Zelda?

Zelda I am old and wise, so listen to me, my children of the earth. There's a place where *all* of us gypsies go to make money. (*Calling*) That place is Epsom Downs!

Gypsies (*nodding in agreement*) Epsom Downs!

Zelda Epsom Downs on Derby Day—and Derby Day is next week! (*Her hands spread out as a pathetic plea*) If only we *could* reach Epsom Downs on Derby Day, then we could make some money!

1st Gypsy But how can we Zelda? It's so far away!

2nd Gypsy Good luck has turned away from us!

3rd Gypsy We are doomed! We are choredo!

Zelda (*angrily*) Don't say that, my child. The Spirit of the Highway watches over us wandering gypsies. He will help us.

1st Gypsy But how?

2nd Gypsy Yes—how?

Zelda We must make a ritual offering to him. Hold out the karri saster, me darling.

The girl holds up the cauldron and Zelda drops the revolting looking props of black sponge, old rags, etc, into it as she takes them from her apron pocket

(*Intoning*) Kereshero, (*pronounced "Kerrez-sherroh"*), I call on you! Great Spirit of the Open Road, look after us, your friends! We offer you dandelions, black nettles, and deadly nightshade!

Gypsies (*whispering*) Deadly nightshade!

Zelda Some harvest corn, some thistles, a dead spider!

Gypsies (*whispering*) A dead spider!

Zelda Ferns, bracken, and five drops of human blood!

Gypsies (*whispering*) Five drops of human blood!

Zelda (*to the girl*) Now, me darling, take the cauldron to the camp fire. (*To the others*) And as the mixture bubbles, recite the Gypsy prayer.

Gypsies (*whispering*) The Gypsy prayer!

Zelda Begone—Baxtiben! Baxtiben! May good fortune somehow come to us!

Gypsies (*holding up their right arms; shouting loudly*) Didicai!

They start to exit

Zelda (*holding her hand up in reply*) Didicai, my darlings, didicai . . . (*Sadly*) If only our prayer could be answered . . . if only we *could* be at Epsom Downs on Derby Day . . . if only we could earn some mazooma . . . but it's not possible . . . we are choredo . . .

The Gypsies exit sadly

Toad, as the washerwoman, breezily enters from the other side, with Dobbin

Toad (*seeing the Gypsies go*) Gypsies! You're in luck Dobbin! They might be able to help you! (*To Zelda*) Good day, my good woman!

Zelda Good day? What's good about it? Pah! (*She spits*)

Toad Well, that's a good start to a conversation, I must say.

Zelda (*deeply suspicious*) You've got a strange voice for a woman, ain't you?

Toad Well, I'm worried you see.

Zelda What you worried about?

Toad I'm lost. Completely and utterly lost. Miles away from where I want to be.

Dobbin neighs and glares at Toad

Oh sorry, Dobbin—this is my old friend Dobbin, and *he's* lost as well! (*Aside; to Zelda*) He doesn't like to be left out, you know.

Zelda has taken a great fancy to Dobbin

Zelda (*patting Dobbin*) Kushti grai! What an intelligent horse you are, to be sure. Greetings, dear! (*To Toad*) It's a kushti, kushti, *kushti* grai you've got there—a very nice horse indeed!

Toad Yes, I've always liked Dobbin. And I'm awfully clever you know. I got him a job pulling my caravan, then I got him a job pulling a barge—then—

Zelda (*with great interest*) Me darling, did you say pulling a *caravan*?

Toad Yes, why?

Zelda We've three caravans, but only two 'orses! We just *got* to reach Epsom Downs to make some money—our lives depend on it—but—but—(*She wipes her eyes with her apron*) The third 'orse was old and he died. We'll never reach Epsom now. (*In despair*) Never.

Toad How utterly amazing! I've just had a good idea—I'm *always* having good ideas—why don't I sell Dobbin to you gypsies?!

The horse glares at him and neighs

Oh! But you'd *like* the gypsy life after that beastly old bargewoman, wouldn't you, Dobbin?

Dobbin neighs and nods his head enthusiastically

I had to ask him his opinion. He doesn't like to be left out, you know.

Zelda, greatly excited, holds out her hands which are trembling violently

Zelda Sell the horse? Kushti! Kushti! Good! Very good!

Toad Then *you* tell me how to find a place called Toad Hall, and *I'll* sell you the horse.

Zelda Follow the path that goes North from the Gypsy Camp and you can't miss it.

Toad Splendid!

Zelda So, what d'you want in exchange for Dobbin?

Toad Some breakfast.

Zelda (*surprised and delighted*) Breakfast in exchange for a horse?

Toad Yes, you see I've run for miles and I'm ravenous.

Zelda Just breakfast?

Toad Well, I suppose I ought to ask *something* for Dobbin. What do you suggest?

Zelda (*looking at Dobbin*) Mmmmmm ... tringrosh ...

Toad Pardon?

Zelda Tringrosh. That's the Romany word for a shilling, and that's my offer. A shillin' a leg.

Dobbin is outraged and shakes his head and stamps

Toad (*surprised*) A shilling a leg? I must work that out and see what it comes to. Now, how many legs has a horse?

Toad points to each leg and then frantically tries to add up with his fingers. Dobbin leans down and puts his mouth towards Toad, who listens

(*Nodding*) That comes to four shillings—I got it straight from the horse's mouth! Har, har, har! (*Realizing*) Four shillings? Great Scott, Dobbin is worth more than that! He's strong and he's very funny you know! Makes me laugh and laugh and laugh, does Dobbin.

Dobbin nods his head and frisks about

Zelda All right then ... five.

Toad Five? What do you think Dobbin?

Dobbin nods

Done! Now to important matters. Where's my breakfast?

Zelda (*staring at Toad; incredulously*) The Gypsy Prayer has been answered! (*She points off*) Go and ask Carla—she'll give you some!

Dobbin glares at Toad, and jumps up and down

Toad Dobbin as well, of course! (*Aside; to Zelda*) He doesn't like to be left out, you know.

Zelda Carla will look after both of you. (*She hands money to Toad*) Here's your five shillings. I must be mad to buy it from you for so much money.

Toad Yes, you must! Oh, I knew I'd strike a good bargain—I always do! Happy, Dobbin?

Dobbin nods

Then come on, breakfast—beautiful, beautiful breakfast! Then I really must get back to dear old Toad Hall.

Singing happily his "Toad Song"—Song 2—Toad exits with Dobbin

As Toad goes Zelda lifts up her head, lets out a great cackle of laughter, pulls up her skirts and jigs about like a ten-year-old

Zelda Ha ha ha! I've got a horse! I've got a kushti grai! (*Calling off*) Romani! Gitani! Our prayers are answered! (*Louder*) Hosati! Hosati! Laugh and be happy!

The Tabs open or the frontcloth is flown to reveal the permanent set with a cut-out of a caravan in it, some ragged laundry on a line, a camp fire etc—the Gypsy camp itself

> *All the Gypsy tribe enter but they look at the ground and shake heads, much distressed*

Zelda (*waving her pipe at them*) Cheer up, cherubs! We got a horse! We're going to Epsom after all! We're going to make some money! We're going to be Barrolo—we're going to be rich!

Gypsies (*delighted, turning to each other*) Barrolo!

1st Gypsy (*clapping her hands, stamping feet—tango style*) Bravo barrolo!

2nd Gypsy (*to the others*) We got a horse!

3rd Gypsy Good luck has come!

Zelda It is years since we gypsies danced—but now we own a new horse! Now we must celebrate!

The Gypsies take partners

> Remember the Gypsy blood in your veins and dance a Cachucha, the Gypsy Dance of Happiness!

Gypsies (*variously; shouting over the music introduction*) Romano!
Romani!
Hosati!
Kheliken!
Didicai!
Barvalo!

Maybe Dobbin has entered during this and is patted by Zelda, and all now sing and clap hands in the flamenco gypsy style.

Everyone sings Song 9 and during the song two Gypsies come CS and face each other, Spanish style, and do some exaggerated flamenco steps. Others produce castanets and maraccas

Song 9 (Parody from "The Gondoliers")

All

> Dance a Cachucha, Fandango, Bolero
> Gypsies let's drink up a wine from Montero
> Wine, when it flows in abundance, enhances
> The reckless delight of this wildest of dances
> To the pitter—pitter—pitter—patter
> And the clitter—clitter—clitter—clatter
> Pitter—pitter—patter
> Clitter—clitter—clatter
> Clitter—clitter—clatter
> Pitter—pitter—patter
> To the pitter—pitter—pitter—patter
> And the clitter—clitter—clitter—clatter
> Patter—patter—patter
> Patter—patter—patter
> Patter, we'll dance!

So Gypsies, let's drink up a wine from Montero
And play a guitar that entrances
Or shake a Maracca, you wild gypsy cracker
And play through the night
With the stars shining bright
Let us all hit the height
As we sing and we fight
In this wildest of Gypsy dances!
Oley!

Production Routine

To help the scene change, it is best (after the dance itself has ended) to bring the Gypsies downstage and close the Tabs behind them. Then the Gypsies line the footlights, down on one bended knee, and get the Audience to clap in time as they reprise some of the number and then they stand again and into a flamenco style pose for the applause

There is a Black-out

The Gypsies exit one side, as Badger enters the other, still in front of the Tabs or frontcloth, holding an open newspaper. He is mournful. A spotlight picks him up

Badger (*declaiming to the Audience, shaking his head*) Poor Toad! I knew his father, I knew his grandfather, I knew his Uncle the Archdeacon! (*He holds up the newspaper*) It says in the *Chronicle* that the Chief Weasel and his followers have left the Wild Wood and are "on manoeuvres". I don't like the sound of that. This is an occasion when we need someone reckless to think up some reckless plan. (*He shakes his head gloomily*) Toad would have been ideal, but alack, alack, it's not to be. I knew his father, I knew his grandfather, I knew his . . .

Ratty and Mole enter, Ratty carrying a big holdall or cricket bag, Mole with an open newspaper

Ratty (*cheerfully*) Belay there, Badger!
Mole (*urgently*) Badger, have you seen the *Chronicle*? It says that the Weasels are advancing! (*His toes turn in and he bites his nails in fright*) Oh my! Oh my! Oh my!
Badger Yes, Mole, it's very worrying. *We* may be all right, but who's going to look after the Rabbits? They're not a very intelligent bunch you know. Who's going to defend *them*?
Ratty I can supply the arms! (*He waves the holdall*)
Mole (*excitedly*) Arms? Oh my! Oh my! Oh my!
Badger I remember you supplied the picnic, and a very good picnic it was. But this isn't a picnic.
Mole No. (*Timidly and somewhat feebly*) This is war!

Ratty holds up the holdall and clanks it about—the noise is impressive

Ratty Don't worry, everything's in here. I've worked it all out. We each need a compass, a policeman's truncheon, a set of handcuffs, some bandages and sticking plaster, a flask of hot tea, some Marmite sandwiches, a pair of binoculars, and some warm underwear—d'you think that'll be enough?

Mole (*flabbergasted*) Enough?

Badger I can stand still with all that on my back, but how am I going to *move forward*?

Ratty I'll give you a push in the direction of the enemy.

Mole (*laughing*) Ratty, you do say some funny things!

Badger Mole, this is serious. I think we should go to the Riverbank and boost up the Rabbits' morale.

Ratty They're terrified of the Weasels.

Mole And what about the Field-mice? They run about in all directions whether there's a war on or not.

Badger Then it's onwards to the Rabbits and the Field-mice at the Riverbank.

Ratty (*with romantic ecstasy*) Back home to the Riverbank! Fresh air, waves on the water, and messing about in boats! There is *nothing*—absolutely nothing—half so much worth doing as simply messing about in boats! (*He mimes rowing*) Heave ho! In out . . . in out . . . in out . . .

The Tabs open to

SCENE 3

The Riverbank again

The Gypsy caravan has been removed. Sitting on the log, waiting impatiently are the Policeman with his helmet off, mopping his brow with a handkerchief, and the Magistrate

Ratty moves backwards, upstage, with enthusiastic rowing actions, and then bumps into the Magistrate and Policeman

Ratty In out . . . in out . . . in out . . . good rowing . . . good rowing . . . good rowing . . . (*Seeing Policeman and Magistrate*) Good heavens! It's you!

Magistrate (*drily*) Yes, it's me. (*To Mole and Badger*) I'm afraid I recognize you two as well.

The Policeman puts his helmet on and does his knees bend movements

Policeman We're here because that friend of yours—the prisoner called Toad—is bound to return to 'is old 'aunts. Convicts always do. So if we waits 'ere long enough, we'll be able to nick 'im.

Mole Your Honour, you must forgive me, I'm only a mole, but Mr Toad is innocent.

Magistrate It could be, it could be. It's an interesting case.

Policeman Don't make me laugh. (*He points to Mole*) I meant 'im sir, not you sir.

Magistrate (*tetchily*) I'm glad you did, Constable. (*To the others*) I'm here because I'm worried. In my Courtroom, justice must be seen to be done. But at Toad's Trial my Clerk of the Court behaved like a nincompoop.

The Policeman laughs smugly

So did you.

The Policeman stops laughing

Policeman Yes sir. (*To the others*) I feel I must elucidate. What 'appened was this. (*He does "knees bend" movements*) The Clerk and me checked on Toad, but unfortunately we thought Toad was *another* Toad. We thought Toad was the notorious criminal Toad what's been wanted by Scotland Yard for some considerable time. Now *that* Toad isn't the same Toad as this Toad. This Toad is *your* Toad, whereas *that* Toad is another Toad. *That* Toad is the Toad what is easily recognizable 'cos 'es got blue tattoos all over his arms. (*With a triumphant finish to his speech*) In other words, a case of Mistaken Identity! (*He bows*) I thank you.

Badger, Mole and Ratty applaud

(*Triumphantly*) All clear now?
Badger, Mole and Ratty *No.*
Magistrate (*wearily*) I think I'd better take over, Constable. The other Toad is a common criminal who is covered in blue tattoos and is known in the trade as "Toad the Woad".
Badger, Mole and Ratty (*now understanding*) Ah!
Policeman (*amused at the memory*) Oh dear me, we was all finkin' of the wrong Toad at the Trial, wasn't we sir?
Magistrate We was—were. And when you're thinking of the *wrong* Toad, twenty years imprisonment is too long a sentence. Far too long a sentence.
Mole (*encouraging him*) Oh it is, Your Honour, it is.
Ratty (*excitedly to Badger, as an aside*) I think he's changed tack! I think there's fine weather ahead!
Badger (*nodding*) So do I, Ratty. (*To the Magistrate and Policeman in his usual drone*) Toad did wrong, we know that. But he's a good sort is Toad, and it will interest you to know that honesty runs in his family. Ah me, I knew his father, I knew his grandfather, I knew his Uncle the Archdeacon.
Mole That's too long a sentence as well.
Ratty Badger, *do* stop mentioning the Archdeacon.
Magistrate (*starting*) Archdeacon Toad?
Badger Yes.
Magistrate Archdeacon *Timothy* Toad?
Badger Yes. No longer with us I fear.
Magistrate (*excitedly*) He was a great friend of mine. So Timothy was Toad's uncle! A fine family!
Mole Your Honour, I hope it's not impertiment to put my snout in like this, but could we come back to the Courtroom and have a chat?

Magistrate It is possible. Toad the Woad is a top criminal—the best of his class—as a matter of fact I have a signed photograph of him tucked into me bedroom mirror—(*Condescendingly*)—but *your* Toad isn't a *patch* on the other Toad, is he?

Badger, Mole and Ratty (*eagerly*) Oh no, no, no, no!

Magistrate Now Toad *the Woad* wants putting away for life, if the Police can ever catch him.

Policeman (*miserably*) We do our best. (*With a knees bend*) Toads and frogs drive me hopping mad.

Magistrate But Toad of *Toad Hall* is a mere petty criminal ...

Badger (*shaking his head*) I knew his father, I knew his grandfather ...

Magistrate Well *I* knew his Uncle, the Archdeacon. Dear old Timothy Toad. We were at school together! It's a small world ... (*To the Policeman*) Am I free next Tuesday afternoon?

Policeman (*whipping out his notebook and checking*) No, me lud.

Magistrate Fiddlesticks. (*To Ratty, Mole and Badger*) I'll see you next Tuesday at three. (*Kindly*) How does this suit you—his dungeon sentence is *reduced to a fine*?

Badger, Mole and Ratty (*delighted*) Fine!

Magistrate (*with irritation*) That's what I said, fine, there's no need to repeat it.

Policeman (*ushering the Magistrate out*) Fancy us putting the Toad in a dungeon when we didn't oughter 'ave done. I sometimes fink the law is a ass.

Magistrate Well, you should know. (*With a strange laugh*) Huh! Huh! Huh! (*He turns back to Ratty, Mole and Badger*) Next Tuesday at three—and I'll give you some tea. (*He removes his judge's wig cheerfully, as though a hat*) Good day gentlemen!

The Policeman and Magistrate exit

On the other side Toad's head with the washerwoman's hat on (but at a rakish angle) pops round the scenery

Toad (*to himself*) All clear! (*He steps forward and addresses the Audience*) My three comrades—and they'll *never* recognize me in this cunning disguise!!!

Ratty, Mole and Badger react with joy and great surprise

Badger My dear friend!

Ratty Shipmate!

Mole Toad!

Toad (*disappointedly*) Oh. (*Emotionally*) Fellows ... Badger, Ratty, dear old Mole ... I can't tell you how good it is to see you three again ... (*He starts to warm up*). I have just escaped, by my great daring and cleverness, from a dismal dungeon full of bats and beetles and clanking chains and— (*He suddenly remembers and is frightened*)—that was the Magistrate! He'll be back in a minute!

Mole Badger, tell Toad the good news!

Badger Ah me, you unhappy animal. Careering about the countryside dressed up as a washerwoman. To think you should have sunk to this.

Toad Sunk? I haven't sunk to anything! I'm Toad!

Ratty Go on Badger, we *want* you to say it this time!

Badger (*in his usual drone*) I knew your father, I knew your grandfather (*with great emphasis*), I knew your *Uncle the Archdeacon*.

Ratty (*ecstatically*) Beautiful words, beautiful!

Toad I don't quite follow . . .

Mole Your uncle was a friend of the Magistrate! It's broken the ice! We're to go back to the Courtroom and explain things, and clear your name!

Badger The Magistrate mistook you. He thought you were someone called Toad the Woad.

Toad (*utterly disgusted*) Toad the Woad? I'm Toad the Tremendous—Toad the Triumphant! All my worries are over! (*He paces about, very full of himself now*) And I've been through such trials since I last saw you, you can't think! Such worries, such sufferings and all so nobly borne! Such escapes, such disguises, and all so perfectly planned!

Badger, Mole and Ratty (*fed up—quietly*) Toad.

Toad (*with more pacing about*) Been in prison—got out of it of course! Sold Dobbin to some gypsies! Sold him for a fortune, needless to say!

Badger, Mole and Ratty (*louder*) Toad!

Toad Oh, I *am* a smart Toad, and no mistake! What d'you think my last exploit was? Just hold on while I tell you . . .

Badger, Mole and Ratty (*very loudly*) TOAD!

Toad (*rather hurt*) My dear fellows, I'm making a speech of *thanks*! You've cleared my name with the Magistrate! We must celebrate! Everybody come back to Toad Hall at once! I can't wait to see the dear old place again! Come on fellows! (*He starts to exit*) Well, come on! (*Pause*) What's the matter?

Badger (*awkwardly*) We hardly dare tell you, you've had such a bad time of it, and you're a good hearted animal.

Ratty There are storms ahead, the ship is on the rocks, but somehow you must be brave.

Mole You see Toad, we were so worried about you being in prison—as were all the Rabbits and Field-mice and everyone—that we never thought—we never realized . . .

Toad Well go on . . . you can tell me!

Badger Taking advantage of the fact that you were locked up in that dreadful dungeon, the Chief Weasel led forth his followers from out the Wild Wood, and . . . and . . .

Ratty They've taken Toad Hall.

There is a terrible silence. Toad receives this news badly and is shattered

Toad (*almost in a whisper*) Taken my home? My lovely home? And it's *your* home as well! Because you're always welcome at Toad Hall, you know that, and the Rabbits, the Field-mice, the Squirrels, they all love visiting me at Toad Hall and . . . and . . . everyone's welcome at anytime . . . (*He bursts into tears and sits down on the log sobbing his heart out*)

Ratty It was a dark night when it happened, blowing hard too, and raining cats and frogs . . .

Mole That's not funny Ratty. Look at poor Toad.

Toad It's all right, Mole. Go on, Ratty, tell me everything. If I lean against there I'll be able to survive—somehow. (*He picks up the log and takes it to a downstage corner and sits on it, his back against the proscenium arch. Emotionally, as he goes*) I must be brave. It's moments like this that make me proud to be a Toad.

The Tabs close or frontcloth is flown in. Downstage, Ratty Mole and Badger act out the capture of Toad Hall for Toad, with dramatic actions and each speech starts with a dramatic music chord, with each chord higher than the last. Ratty speaks as he comes downstage

Ratty A horde of Weasels, armed to the teeth, crept silently along the drive up to the front entrance . . .

Badger Simultaneously, a body of Ferrets, advancing through the kitchen garden, possessed themselves of the back yard . . .

Mole And a company of Stoats, who stuck at nothing, occupied the conservatory . . .

Ratty (*with great indignation*) And they've been in Toad Hall ever since, and going on simply anyhow!

Badger Lying in bed half the day, and breakfast at all hours, and the place is such a mess I'm told it's not fit to be seen!

Mole They've been eating your food, and drinking your drink, and singing bigheaded, boastful songs about—well—prisons and dungeons and Toads.

Toad stands up, heroically

Toad Oh *have* they?! I'll jolly soon see about that! (*He starts to exit*) I'm going home!

Ratty It's no good Toad—one against so many.

Toad (*sadly*) You're right, Ratty.

Badger (*with a sudden outburst*) If you'd behaved yourself, none of this would have happened! Aren't you ashamed of yourself? Crashing the caravan, stealing the car, being flung in the dungeon underneath the castle—

Toad screws up his face during the attack and starts to cry again

Toad Oh . . . oh . . .

Badger (*gasping*) Eureka!!!

Toad Eh?

Badger "Underneath the castle"! That reminds me! (*Impressively*) *Underneath Toad Hall!*

Mole and Ratty What d'you mean?

Badger (*to Toad*) Ah me, I don't know what he would have said, but I knew your father . . .

Mole, Ratty and Toad (*groaning*) Oh, not again!

Badger And I remember he once told me that near here, leading from the river bank to underneath Toad Hall, *there's a secret passage.*

Mole, Ratty and Toad (*eagerly*) A secret passage?

Badger "Don't ever tell my son about it" your father said, "He's a good boy, but he talks too much. It's a secret passage and I want it *kept* secret."

Toad (*pacing about*) Well, well, perhaps I *am* a bit of a talker. A popular fellow such as I am—my friends get round me—we chaff, we sparkle, we tell witty stories—especially me—Har, har har!

Mole Toad, just think of it—a secret passage! Oh my, oh my, oh my!

Badger is not so adventurous

Badger (*cautiously*) But are the four of us prepared to creep along through the darkness that may be swarming with unknown dangers—?

Toad Of course we are! The Count of Monte Cristo did and look what happened to him!

Mole (*eagerly*) What did happen to him?

Toad He discovered Australia!

Badger I don't know about going back to Toad Hall. You ought to be going back to school. Australia indeed. (*Condescendingly*) It was New Zealand.

Toad bends down and rummages in Ratty's holdall

Mole (*shyly*) If it's underground—well—I can see in the dark, you know!

Ratty That'll be a marvellous help, Moley!

Mole (*pleased*) It will?

Badger I know exactly where the passage starts. (*Explaining with big gestures*) It's under one of the willows at the bend in the river. And it ends up under the Butler's Pantry, next to the dining hall!

Toad Aha! That squeaky board in the Butler's Pantry! Now I understand it!

Mole We shall creep out quietly into the Butler's Pantry—

Ratty With our pistols and swords and sticks—

Badger And rush in upon them—

Toad pulls a truncheon from Ratty's bag with a grand flourish

Toad And whack 'em, and whack 'em, and whack 'em, and whack 'em! (*He rushes across the stage fighting imaginary enemies, then stops at the corner and stands on the tree trunk in an heroic pose. Waving the truncheon*) Let's go now!

Ratty, Mole and Badger Yes!

Toad This very minute!

Ratty, Mole and Badger Yes!

Toad Away—to Toad Hall!

Ratty, Mole and Badger (*heroically waving*) To Toad Hall!

A loud fanfare is played and Ratty, Mole and Badger all rush off, following Toad, waving their arms and shouting excitedly

At once there is sleezy music, and at the opposite corner the Chief Weasel enters in a green spotlight. He casually leans against the proscenium and sarcastically raises his wine goblet to the Audience

Chief Weasel Cheers! This is a beautiful brandy from Toad's wine cellar. (*He sniffs it like a connoisseur, then chokes violently*) Oh, I am enjoying myself living here at Toad Hall. This place is what the estate agents call a "desirable residence" and it's even more desirable now that it's packed with weasels and ferrets and stoats. Yes, I've terrorized the local population and now I've moved in here I'm going to celebrate my reign of terror by giving a little party in the dining hall. (*He beckons off*) Come my ferrets and weasels! There's food and drink and it's all free, so come to the ball!

The Tabs open, or the Woodland frontcloth is flown

SCENE 4

Inside Toad Hall

Jury benches from the Courtroom have been set each side of the long table and the Courtroom heraldry is reversed so that it is now a green shield with a Toad face on it, and the words "Toad For Ever" as a motto underneath

The Wicked Animals are on stage and sing and dance Song 10

Note: If this production number is to be the dramatic tango "Jealousy", then the Chief Weasel's speech needs to have ended with:

Chief Weasel There's food and drink, there's beautiful bedrooms, there's a gorgeous garden—no wonder I'm jealous! All my life I've been jealous of Toad and what is it that has spurred me on to take over Toad Hall? You're right ... it's ... Jealousy!!!

Song 10 (Production Number)

The Ferret, Stoat and Weasel families sing and dance. They are all ages, and it's a loud and vicious routine of triumph

After the song they sit at the banqueting table while the Chief Weasel jumps on a bench then on to the table. He holds up his hand for silence

Chief Weasel My foul and ferocious friends!
All (*waving mugs and goblets*) 'Ere! 'Ere!
Chief Weasel It's time to celebrate! Have you all had enough to eat and drink?
All (*waving mugs*) Yus!

1st Weasel stands up and pats his stomach. He is obviously full of food

1st Weasel Ooooo-yes!
Chief Weasel Good! Eat your fill! I know you're a Weasel but make a *pig* of yourself!

They all laugh in a boozy way

Now I don't want to detain you from grabbing even *more* grub—
All (*laughing*) Oooooooo!
Chief Weasel But before I resume my seat—

1st Ferret suddenly stands up waving his mug

1st Ferret (*squeakily*) 'Oooooooray!
Chief Weasel Cuthbert, be quiet.

1st Ferret sits

I should like to say one word about our kind host, Mr Toad ...
All (*sarcastically*) Good old Toady! Ha, ha, ha—cheers!
Chief Weasel Yes, good old Toady, without whom the sausage rolls, the
   trifle, the fruit cake, and the ice cream gateau that you've just guzzled,
   could not have happened!
All (*waving their mugs drunkenly*) True, true! 'Ere, 'ere! Ooooooray!
Chief Weasel I've set up my headquarters here and I'm going to rule over
   the rabbits, scare the squirrels and frighten the field-mice into submission!
   And where is their friend and champion, Toad? Where d'you think?
All In the clink!
Chief Weasel (*nodding*) Correct! So now I'm going to sing you a little song
   all about my enemy. (*He sings unaccompanied, to the tune of "Little Brown
   Jug"*)

> Toad is stupid
> Toad is vain
> Toad is brainless
> Toad's a pain
> Toad is fat
> And Toad is plain
> I hope Toad goes down the drain!

*The Chief Weasel conducts as they all sing, swaying to and fro, chanting
boozily and banging their mugs on the table in time*

All together now!—If you're not too full of food and drink to manage it!
All   Oooooooh,
> Toad is stupid
> Toad is vain
> Toad is brainless
> Toad's a pain
> Toad is—

*There is a loud crash from percussion, dramatic duelling music such as the
"William Tell Overture", and Badger rushes in waving his cudgel. He stands
posed. The assembly is greatly surprised*

Badger (*shouting*) The hour has come! (*He starts to hit the Weasels with his
cudgel*) And we'll whack 'em, and whack 'em, and whack 'em!

Mole rushes in waving a wooden sword and stands posed

Mole (*shouting*) A mole! A mole! (*He also starts to hit the Weasels*) And we'll whack 'em, and whack 'em, and whack 'em!

Ratty rushes in waving a dagger and stands posed

Ratty (*shouting*) Belay there! Belay there, me hearties! (*He also hits the Weasels*) And we'll whack 'em, and whack 'em, and whack 'em!

Toad now rushes in and poses with a large scimitar held on high

Toad England expects every man this day will do his duty! (*Waving the scimitar about, far away from anyone, though thoroughly enjoying himself*) And we'll whack 'em, and whack 'em, and whack 'em!

The Ferrets and Weasels, surprised, cry out and cower in fear

Ferrets and Weasels (*variously*) No!
Help!
What's happening?!
I surrender!
That hurt!
Save me!
Mercy!
OW!

Chief Weasel (DS, *over the noise*) Weasels! Rally round! Never surrender! (*Shouting*) You cowards!

Toad (*to Chief Weasel*) So *you're* the Wicked Weasel! We meet at last!

The two sworn enemies face each other, Toad holding his scimitar, the Chief Weasel holding a stick. Everyone else stops their fighting to watch

Chief Weasel (*sneering*) Toad, how I *hate* you. I've only one thing to say to you and that is . . .

Toad lifts the enormous scimitar in the air, about to crash it down

HELP! MERCY! (*He kneels down, hands clasped together in prayer, terrified*)

Toad You cringeing creature, do you promise that you'll never again try to invade the valley, conquer the countryside and rule over the Riverbank?

Chief Weasel Yes!

Badger (*to his cowering group*) *You* surrender?

Weasels Yes!

Mole (*to his group*) *You* surrender?

Weasels Yes!

Ratty *You* surrender?

Weasels Yes!

Toad (*to the Chief Weasel*) And do *you* surrender?

Chief Weasel No!

Toad waves his scimitar threateningly again

Yes!

Toad (*to all*) Get to the back of the room, you crummy collection of animals! For I am the Toad! The happy, the glorious, the completely victorious, Toad!

The Weasels, Stoats and Ferret families clutch at each other and retreat upstage as Badger, Ratty and Mole threaten them

Toad moves CS *and speaks out front*

Unaccustomed as I am to public speaking—har, har, har!—nevertheless I have here a few notes on the subject of Toad's Tremendous Victory. (*He pulls a huge untidy batch of papers from his pocket*) There was Alexander the Great, William the Conqueror, Christopher Columbus, Lord Nelson, Sir Lancelot—but not one of these compares to Toad. Toad the incredible, Toad the invincible, Toad the ...

Ratty (*calling out, desperately*) Badger, stop him!

Badger You're right Ratty! (*With usual droning and head shaking*) Ah me, I knew his father, I knew his grandfather, I knew his Uncle the Arch ...

Ratty (*calling*) Mole, stop them *both*!

Mole Stop them both? Oh my, oh my, oh my!

Ratty (*fed up*) Mole! You three are impossible, so *I* will sing the song of victory. One, two, three ...

Song 11: parody of "Phil The Fluter"

(*Singing*)	There was panic in the parlour
	And a howling in the hall
	There was crying in the cowshed
	And a shrieking in the stall
	There was smashing in of window
	And a crashing in of door
	There were weasels and some ferrets
	Who had fainted on the floor!
Mole	The Trumpeters are tooting
	And the soldiers are saluting—oh
	The cannons are all shooting
	And some of them explode.
Badger	The Rabbits are all rooting
	And the motor cars are hooting
	And I'm sure that Phil is fluting
	At the Victory for Toad
Toad	The frogs have started hopping
	And they're shouting out for joy
	The mice are all be-bopping
	Every girl and every boy
	The stoats have started stoating
	And I think the wine has flowed
	Oh, everyone's emoting
	At the Victory for Toad
All	Oh everyone's emoting

> At the Victoreeeeee—
> For Toad!!!!

A short "Irish Jig" routine follows

The Chief Weasel and his followers reprise the song and dance as a jig, while Toad, Ratty, Mole and Badger are at the footlights, encouraging the Audience to clap along with the tempo

At the Coda, all pose for the final moment. Ratty and Mole on each side of Toad lift him up on their shoulders and he waves to the Audience

All   Oh everyone's emoting
                                  At the Victoreeeee—
                                  The Victoreeee—
                                  The Victoreeee—
                                  For Toad!

The CURTAIN *falls*

The five principals (Toad, Mole, Ratty, Badger and the Chief Weasel) exit quickly

The CURTAIN *rises*

There is a reprise of Song 5. The Cast, as they take their bows, ensure that the Audience claps along

First the Weasel, Ferret, and Stoat families take their bow. Then the minor principals. Then the Chief Weasel, Badger, Mole and Ratty respectively

Now Toad enters behind the cut-out of the motor car, once again wearing his motoring cap, motoring coat and big gauntlets and waving

Toad (*as he arrives*) Poop, poop! Poop, poop!
All (*through cupped hands, laughing*) Poop, poop! Poop, poop!

The Company sings some of Song 5 at half tempo, doing ragtime kick movements

All   A dozen times he'd start to hug and kiss
                                  And then the darned old engine, it would miss
                                  And then he'd have to get under
                                  Get out and get under
                                  To fix up his automobile!

CURTAIN

*NOTE: As Toad steps from behind the cut-out of the motor car at the finale, you may like Portly Otter to present him with a box that has a big bow on it, like some elaborate present. Toad opens it and, delighted, takes out of the box a model aeroplane, calling out: "*Another craze! I say, what a marvellous method of transport!*" and holding it up, he "dive bombs" the period aeroplane, making big circles and suitable zooming aeroplane noises. Then the Company starts to sing over his zooming noises the final song, as already explained*

FURNITURE AND PROPERTY LIST

Only essential properties are listed here, as mentioned in the text. Further dressing may be added at the Producer's discretion

See also scenery notes which follow these plots

ACT I

SCENE 1

Off stage: Picnic basket **(Ratty)**
Union Jack **(Field-mouse)**
Small flags **(Juvenile animals)**
Door mat (set in wings for **Mole**)
Goggles, check cap, gauntlet gloves, motoring coat **(Toad)**

Personal: **Mrs Otter:** handkerchief
Ratty: nautical cap
Mole: bucket with white-wash in it and brush
Toad: shilling, whistle on string around neck
Reginald: spanner
Animals: straw boaters or parasols

SCENES 2 and 3

Off stage: Bowl and spoon **(Jenny)**
Handcuffs, chains, ropes **(Nellie)**

Personal: **Clerk:** hand bell, list
Magistrate: roll of parchment, whistle, yellow card
Policeman: huge keys on a ring
Toad: handcuffs, money

ACT II

SCENE 1

Off stage: Wash tub. *In it:* huge packet of soap powder **(Bargewoman)**
Washing **(Animals)**
Sixpences **(Animals)**

Personal: **Weasel:** map
Bargewoman: shawl, sugar

Scene 2

On stage: cauldron

Off stage: Castanets and maraccas **(Gypsies)**
Newspaper **(Badger)**
Holdall. *In it:* truncheon and other weapons **(Ratty)**
Newspaper **(Mole)**

Personal: **Zelda:** pipe, apron. *In apron pocket:* black/green props for "ingredients",
money

Scene 3

Off stage: Goblet **(Chief Weasel)**

Personal: **Policeman:** handkerchief, notebook
Toad: papers

Scene 4

On stage: Jury benches
"Toad" heraldic shield
Table loaded with food
Mugs and goblets for Weasel and Stoats
Stick for Chief Weasel

Off stage: Cudgel **(Badger)**
Wooden sword **(Mole)**
Dagger **(Ratty)**
Scimitar **(Toad)**

LIGHTING PLOT

Various interior and exterior settings

ACT I, SCENE 1

To open: Afternoon sunlight

| Cue 1 | **As Animals** exit | (Page 2) |
| | *Lights darken. Green spot on Chief Weasel* | |

| Cue 2 | **Chief Weasel** exits | (Page 3) |
| | *Lights return to normal* | |

| Cue 3 | **Mrs Otter** enters | (Page 10) |
| | *Lights darken to sinister level* | |

| Cue 4 | **As Mrs Otter** and **Mole** hide | (Page 11) |
| | *Lightning, then Lights dim* | |

| Cue 5 | **Wicked Animals** shout and stamp | (Page 12) |
| | *Strobe lighting* | |

| Cue 6 | After Song 3 | (Page 12) |
| | *Strobe ceases* | |

| Cue 7 | After **Wicked Animals** exit | (Page 12) |
| | *Revert to normal lighting* | |

| Cue 8 | **Reginald:** "Police! Police!" (2nd time) | (Page 21) |
| | *Black-out* | |

ACT I, SCENE 2

To open: General lighting

No cues

ACT II, SCENE 1

To open: Afternoon sunlight

| Cue 9 | **As Rabbits** and **Bargewoman** exit | (Page 35) |
| | *Lights darken, green spot on Chief Weasel* | |

| Cue 10 | **As Chief Weasel** swaggers off | (Page 35) |
| | *Return to normal* | |

EFFECTS PLOT

ACT I

SCENERY SUGGESTIONS

The scenery presents no problems. You may wish for a spectacular production but if a smaller one is required, these notes will help, as they allow for a permanent set.

As the story is a fantasy about animals that speak, the entire play can take place in this permanent set or even studio style in-the-round, with no scenery. The few essentials (caravan, Courtroom benches, dungeon grille with practical door, banqueting room table etc) can easily be brought on by the small-part players who remain in character as, say, Weasels or Rabbits. The Audience enjoys this and it is all part of the entertainment.

To keep the atmosphere of Kenneth Grahame's *The Wind in the Willows* all through, the wings are green/brown weeping willows with the inverted arrow-head-style of leaf formation, and are permanent. The entire adventure story takes place during an Edwardian summer. The cyclorama upstage is also permanent. Or the set can be Woodland/Riverbank with backcloth of trees instead of the cyclorama mentioned. A few times during the play, Tabs or a Woodland frontcloth are needed. Into this permanent set are placed the following:

ACT I
Scene 1—The Riverbank
The permanent willow tree wings are used with, DR, a wide tree trunk painted on the wings. It has a secret panel in it that the audience doesn't notice until it is needed to represent the door to Badger's House. Then part of this tree trunk—like a secret panel—is slid sideways offstage and we see a roughly oval shaped opening through which Badger "enters", as though from his house.

Upstage is the groundrow of rocks and reeds, behind which is Ratty's boat. This groundrow and practical boat are not essential.

Scene 2—Corridor leading to the Courtroom
Tabs or a frontcloth of a corridor with comical portraits of judges and legal notices such as "Wanted" posters on the wall. A chorus song and the Magistrate's song take place in front of the Tabs or frontcloth to allow time for the scene change.

Scene 3(a) and (b)—The Courtroom and Dungeon
Into the woodland set are placed benches arranged up and downstage for the Jury, a simple cut-out for the Magistrate's Desk with a tall stool behind, and a simple cut-out for the witness box. These can be easily set.

Behind the Magistrate is a large heraldic shield—say five feet by four feet—with a motto underneath saying, "JUSTICE?" The shield and motto can be hung from the flies by two wires.

When Toad is marched into the Dungeon, slide a grille on stage from the wings at this moment remembering that there must be a practical door in the grille, and the dungeon scene is played downstage of this grille. Toad sits on a log/tree stump that is used elsewhere, or on one of the Courtroom benches moved to this dungeon area. You may prefer to see the small dungeon set—really just a grille will do—which can be a free standing screen, hinged in the middle already in position as lights come up on the Courtroom Scene.

ACT II
Scene 1—The Canal Bank
The same river groundrow can be used to represent the canal bank, and there is a cut-out of a barge—it doesn't have to move—coming out from the upstage wings. These things are not essential, however.

Scene 2—The Gypsy Camp
This scene begins in a Woodland frontcloth, or Tabs. Then the full-stage is used and in the permanent set are placed a camp fire and cut-out of a gypsy caravan with a line of ragged and picturesque laundry hanging well upstage.

The Gypsy production number that ends this scene is partly performed downstage in front of Tabs (or the Woodland frontcloth) then there is a dialogue scene to allow time for the cut-out caravan etc to be removed and we can return to the permanent full-stage set, which is now:

Scene 3—The Riverbank
Same as for Act I, Scene 1.

Scene 4—Inside Toad Hall
After Scene 3 the Tabs are drawn or frontcloth is flown in, and there is a dialogue scene which is sufficient to allow for setting up the banqueting hall. This can be just a table (preferably refectory style) with Courtroom Jury benches each side, and the heraldic shield from the Courtroom now reversed to show a green shield with the head of Toad on it, or a big Tudor style "T", and the motto underneath is "TOAD FOR EVER". If plenty of food for the table top is needed, then a carefully painted cut-out can stand on the table, conveying the image of big candlesticks, cakes, jellies, trifles, bottles, flowers etc.

PROPERTIES

Ratty's Rowing Boat
If required, he sits on a small box that has four wheels. Nailed on to the front of the box is a cut-out of a blue rowing boat, and to enter, he is either pulled on by a rope or he uses his feet to "walk himself" along. It's best if he *mimes* rowing with oars, and that the cumbersome oars are never seen or

used. It isn't essential to have a boat, though it does help to build Ratty's character.

The 1908 Motor Car
This can be a cut-out of an Edwardian car with its curious proportions and upright steering wheel. The wheels and the doors need not be practical, as the man and girl exit from the car at the upstage side and mime opening and closing the car doors. Perhaps a period motor horn, with a black rubber bulb, that, when pressed, makes almost a "poop, poop" sound, is attached. Either they "carry" the cut-out when they enter (handles attached to the back of the cut-out) or it is pushed on from the wings and we never in fact see the back end of the car. Using this latter method, it can easily be pulled off stage again when Toad reverses it.

The Caravan
If a small or medium sized production, a cut-out that is about eight feet high can be pushed on. No-one need enter the caravan. When it first enters it is "spruce and canary yellow". It has, in fact, various hardboard panels attached to it, and these are the attractive "windows" with shutters and curtains and window box with bright flowers. For the crashed caravan effect, merely remove these panels and they now reveal (underneath) the wrecked window and shutters etc; also the gashed yellow area. Or, use an entirely different cut-out for the "wrecked caravan", which should be at some crazy angle to show it has been knocked over by the passing motor car. In an in-the-round or studio production the yellow caravan must exit before the crash sound effect and the wrecked caravan brought back on.

In Act II, the **Gypsy caravan** is merely a colourful cut-out and from it to the far wing is stretched a laundry line with ragged and patched clothes drying, but the line must be well upstage and away from the dancers in the Gypsy production number.

COSTUMES (DATE–1908)

It's possible to dress all the principal male characters in striped blazers, white trousers, white shirts, and striped ties or bow-ties. Don't use head masks for Toad, Ratty, Badger, Mole and the Chief Weasel as they hide the facial expressions too much. Here are some costume suggestions in more detail:

Toad
Toad wears a green shiny balaclava and animal ears; a green shiny double-breasted coat that is fairly short to allow plenty of leg to show—the frog's legs being green tights. Although huge flippers would be ideal, he will get tired wearing them, so the nearest equivalent to webbed feet is an exaggerated version of Tudor shoes, like Henry VIII wore, in green of course. A green shirt, big green bow-tie, green gloves that are also shiny. His make-up is green, but prominently lined eyes are needed. A huge slash of a mouth in bright red, turned up at the sides, far bigger than the actor's real mouth, so

that it looks like a slice of melon. His Edwardian motoring gear is exactly as shown in the illustrations to *The Wind in the Willows*, which are a great help for all costumes.

Ratty
Ratty wears white flannels, with his long rat's tail sticking out, white shirt sleeves rolled up (see the book's illustrations). Or a seaman's thick white pullover or a merchant navy jacket, jeans and wellies or sometimes white plimsoles. Out of the seat of the jeans sticks his long tail which he picks up and points with whenever emphasizing something. Make-up of obvious whiskers on a sunburnt face and maybe a pointed beard.

Rat's ears on his grey balaclava headress and sometimes on top of that a seaman's cap at a jaunty angle. Brown woollen gloves.

Mole
Mole wears glasses with thick frames and probably no lenses, has a pale grey face, black or dark grey corduroy/velvet boiler suit that fits loosely and floppily. A tail and the balaclava-style headress with animal ears should also be black velvet—maybe a continuation of the boiler suit. Black gloves—if possible velvet ones. A scarf of some quiet colour. Sometimes he wears a shabby grey coloured coat.

Badger
Badger is usually a tall lumbering farmer with a brown or dark grey or black tweedy checked Norfolk jacket and "plus fours" and a farmer's clumsy walking stick and boots. A bushy white tail sticks out of the hole in his trousers. His make-up should be bold, and he needs a wig from where the black markings and the two "white streaks" continue down his face. A study of photographs of badgers, plus the helpful illustrations in *The Wind in the Willows* makes this make-up fairly easy. Grey gloves.

The Chief Weasel
The Chief Weasel has a brown face, a flashy orange/brown siren suit/boiler suit, and orange/brown balaclava with ears. From his movements and clothes he is clearly a gangster and can be Teddy-Boy in style, (a parody of correct Edwardian), or even wear a 1920s trilby gangster hat, as long as we remember Kenneth Grahame and don't stray too far from 1908.

Note: All the animals need very prominent out-lining to their eye make-up.

Dobbin The Horse
Dobbin is a pantomime horse.

Reginald and Fiona
They wear Edwardian motoring gear, his being in fact the same as Toad's, that is—large check cap, goggles which are on elastic and can be pushed up, a motoring coat of lightweight material but very long, and huge gauntlet gloves. She wears a very large Edwardian hat with a veil and a full length coat with gauntlet gloves. The hat veil is not over her face.

The Magistrate, Policeman and Clerk
They are as in a Pinero farce such as *The Magistrate* or Gilbert and Sullivan's *Trial by Jury*. Maybe the Clerk wears glasses on the end of his nose.

Jenny
Jenny wears a simple Edwardian frock, and boots.

Jenny's Aunts
They are Edwardian Cockney washerwomen, like the 1908 flower sellers in Piccadilly Circus, or Eliza Doolittle. Aunt Nellie's clothes are patched, and she later returns in comical Edwardian underwear with plenty of frills on her bloomers and a laced corset.

Mrs Otter
Mrs Otter has a black or brown sleek velvet-style siren suit/boiler suit and balaclava with small ears. Her chest is white. If possible she is sleek and slim but more important is that she is very much the worried and fussy mum.

Young Portly
Portly is a toddler, wears a tiny version of his or her mother's costume—maybe he wears a bush baby jumpsuit.

The Bargewoman
The Bargewoman is a red faced slovenly country woman, with a dirty apron, sleeves rolled up, plimsoles or boots, untidy hair in a bun.

Zelda
Zelda is a lively old gypsy crone, with an upside-down pipe in her mouth, some blacked out teeth, and she wears vivid but patched gypsy clothes.

Chorus Costumes
The Good Animals, Bad Animals and Gypsies are played by both sexes and all ages. The younger Rabbits wear attractive bush baby jumpsuits/play suits/siren suits/boiler suits or brown leotards with powder-puff tails and balaclavas or masks. The older Rabbits can wear Beatrix Potter style costumes. Whiskers are painted on, to be removed when Gypsies.

The younger Weasels wear "wicked and sinister" dark coloured leotards and balaclavas with ears but also need dark coloured domino style masks. The older Weasels wear dark brown canvas shoes, tight brown trousers, brown high necked jerseys and the domino masks—all should have tails and gloves, and balaclavas with ears.

The Gypsies can wear their brightly coloured patched skirts and blouses and waist-coats over the Rabbit or Weasel leotards (but if the Rabbits are Beatrix Potter style, they have to entirely change costumes). The brightly coloured gypsy headscarves have big earrings attached to save time when costume changing.

The Washerwomen (Jenny's Aunts) have a quick change from Animals in
the Courtroom to Washerwomen in the dungeon, but this change is easily
done if long black skirts with elastic top, and blouses and shawls, are worn
over the Animal leotards. Replace the balaclavas with period cockney hats,
or even men's caps of 1908. The Weasels remove their domino masks. The
Rabbits and Weasels concerned with this quick change could wear overcoats and mackintoshes in the Courtroom Scene. They would still have an
animal appearance due to the balaclavas, headresses, masks etc, but the
Cockney washerwomen clothes would be underneath the overcoats for this
quick change.

MADE AND PRINTED IN GREAT BRITAIN BY
LATIMER TREND & COMPANY LTD PLYMOUTH

MADE IN ENGLAND